UNDERST
PARANOIA

UNDERSTANDING PARANOIA

WHAT CAUSES IT, HOW IT FEELS AND WHAT TO DO ABOUT IT

Dr Peter Chadwick

Thorsons
An Imprint of HarperColiins*Publishers*

Thorsons
An Imprint of HarperCollins*Publishers*
77/85 Fulham Palace Road,
Hammersmith, London W6 8JB
1160 Battery Street,
San Francisco, California 94111–1213
Published by Thorsons 1995
1 3 5 7 9 10 8 6 4 2

A catalogue record for this book is available from the British Library

ISBN 0 7225 3023 4

Printed in Great Britain by HarperCollinsManufacturing Glasgow.

CONTENTS

The same process which makes us able to see meaning and order in life, and to make new discoveries, also makes us very vulnerable to mistaken beliefs — especially as the vulnerability increases with the ability to comprehend and so with intelligence!

Hans Eysenck and David Nias
Astrology — Science or Superstition?
(Penguin Books, 1984)

INTRODUCTION

Paranoia is a significant problem in Western society today, particularly in busy towns and cities. Approximately one-tenth of all hospital admissions for mental disorder involve paranoia in some way. When we consider that at some time in their lives, roughly one in nine men and one in six women require specialist professional treatment for psychological problems, it is clear that paranoia is a difficulty that affects hundreds of thousands of people to a degree where they can reasonably be said to be *ill* with this complaint.

Paranoia is something we have probably all experienced in different ways but it reaches its greatest level of malignancy and distress in *paranoid schizophrenia*. It is probably true that for most people the paranoid schizophrenic and the paranoid psychotic person are together the very prototype of what they take a 'mad' person to be. The idea of the 'maniac' is another prototype which colours the thinking of lay people when they think or talk of 'insanity'.

This book discusses the subject of paranoia generally and also attempts to relate the mind of the psychotic to that of so-called normal, sane people. I shall try to give an understanding of 'madness' by focusing on its most common form of expression — suspicion in a context of *extreme* self consciousness. Suspicion itself is something well known to both sane and insane, and so perhaps is a useful bridge to connect the two worlds. To be paranoid, in itself, is not at all the same as to be mad; but it is an experience which perhaps enables us to sympathize and empathize a little with those, alas, who are.

Interestingly, paranoia and mania, as we will see, are closely related — indeed some would say indistinguishable. The lay prototypes do, indeed, reflect an intuitive grasp of the deeper commonalities that bind these disorders together. Paranoids are often manic to some degree, manics often paranoid. When we talk of these illnesses we are close to the core of what everyone means by madness.

It is important, however, to express at the outset what I am trying to do in this book. My critical purpose is to give lay people, many of whom will either be sufferers or who will have close or occasional contact with such people, knowledge and information to enhance their own understanding and their ability to cope with the effects and the threat of paranoia. Personally, I feel that there is little doubt that genetic factors in part underpin this group of problems. But an academic understanding of genetics is not appropriate for everyone. What is needed is information that is practically effective and which can be understood and easily digested. The book is therefore designed for 'easy reading', without descending to a level which insults the reader's intelligence.

Developments in recent years have clearly shown that the thoughts, experiences and behaviour of the psychotic person and of 'borderline' individuals are on a continuum with those of normal people: they are not produced by completely separate and different processes. The 'mad' are therefore of the same ilk as all of us. Indeed madness is now recognized as being, like extroversion and neuroticism, a group of underlying dimensions to personality resulting in a tendency which is latent, to a greater or lesser extent, in everyone: but which can 'explode' into bizarre behaviour if the stresses are too high and a person's coping skills too weak.

It is also now recognized that the same processes that lead to very serious delusions can, under different circumstances and in different contexts, lead to creativity and to high achievement. The very expression of psychosis can in itself be a creative act of a kind; although it is more difficult to empathize with than the usual offerings deemed by our culture to be creative. Because of this, insanity has a positive aspect as well as a negative side to be taken into account. In my view, the continual harping on the deficits and character weaknesses of the insane, to be found in some quarters, is often biased and misplaced.

It is outdated now to regard the thinking of the insane as 'quintessentially *un*understandable'. Such concepts further estrange sufferers who are already alienated anyway and they are obviously unenlightening. In this book I will try to take the reader into the world of the bizarre to show how perhaps *nothing* in the psychotic mind is really totally beyond our powers to explain. This journey may be strange but, in the end, hopefully informative.

There has never been a better time to be a psychologist working on schizophrenia and paranoia. Psychological research is, at last, beginning to bear fruit and is revealing new ways for helping sufferers. The laudable efforts to prise open the secrets of paranoia at a genetic and biochemical level are valuable, but leave largely unstated how these processes really do account for the experiences of the sufferer on a day-to-day basis. Sociological accounts similarly deal with the kinds of social stresses that can precede psychosis but, again, how these operate within the mind of the victim is left unstated.

We cannot continue to leave the paranoid person as a kind of 'hole in theoretical space', bumped around by genetic biases (and pills) on the one hand, and life events (and community care programmes) on the other; but, through unwillingness to get under their skin, say nothing about what is actually *going on in their minds* – in a way that they can assimilate and relate to. This is the critical function of psychology in this context.

However, we must also be prepared not only to analyse but to *write* about the paranoid world without all colour and warmth being drained away merely to appear 'objective'. One of the most obvious features of works on paranoia and schizophrenia (whether they are on causes, prevention, treatment, description or whatever) is the singular coldness of the texts. Here we are dealing with one of the most emotional, quite devastating, experiences any human being can undergo and the whole topic is traditionally discussed with the clinical frigidity appropriate to a learned anatomical study of the fish. The authors never make the reader hear a single note of the tragic 'music' they describe.

With the continued closure of mental hospitals, people previously diagnosed as mentally ill are all about us – on buses, trains, in parks and on street corners. They are no longer shut away so that we can deny their existence. Many return to their homes and live with their families; others are in hotels, hostels – or sleeping in cardboard boxes. Altogether they are in our midst. The future for the care of the recovering mentally ill is community care, not asylum care. But if we *are* to care for and be fair with these people, we must have an understanding of them and not regard them as biblical lepers or freaks – which they are not. This book is an attempt to bring the sane and the insane closer together and to bridge the 'cold air' between them – cold air that is felt on *both* sides, especially by the paranoid. In addition we must cure our own 'paranoia' about the mentally ill; and perhaps a good place to start is by looking at this very process which, at some time in our lives, has touched us all.

———————

This book is oriented largely towards the *psychological* understanding of paranoia in its many forms, ranging from normal anxiety through to psychosis. There is much that has been learned about this at a neurochemical, behavioural and sociological level which is omitted here; but the reader can find treatments that go outside the area of psychology in parts of the 'further reading' list at the end of the book. I am not attempting to be exhaustive – such writers, as Oscar Wilde said, are usually *exhausting*. I will, however, make frequent reference to three factors that are emerging in psychological research on paranoia: biases in the way paranoia sufferers deal with new information; biases in what they *attribute* events to; and pathological factors in the family or relationship atmosphere. Problems in these areas crop up over and over again in clinical work with individual clients, so reference will be made to them in several areas of the text.

I must say finally that this book could not have been written without the continued support, and the reactions, of my students, friends and colleagues. I am particularly grateful to Richard Bentall of Liverpool University, Gordon Claridge of Oxford University and Hans Eysenck and Brian Foss of London University, for their endorsement and encouragement of the approach I am taking here, which is based on research I began in 1979/80. John Wilding and

David Nias, also of London University, have in addition been willing ears to these ideas for some time.

The book has also grown out of the innumerable discussions of a small band of my closest friends and I, who decided to form ourselves into a group which we call 'The Borderliners'. This is a post-therapy group that meets regularly at the Royal Festival Hall and the Café Royal in London over tea and snacks. Apart from myself the group comprises, as core members: Simon Blair (a Transactional Analyst), Geoff Garfield (a sociologist), Jane Howe (an English Literature graduate), Des Marshall (a mystic and prose-poet), Jonathan Smith (a lecturer in psychology at Birkbeck College and a Gestalt therapist) and Ivo Wiesner (a musician and spiritual healer). At every meeting one or two guests are invited and over the years of the group's existence a steady flow of interesting and remarkable people have gladdened our ears and eyes. The group has also benefitted from the ideas of Ron Clarke, who has acted as 'roving correspondent' on economics, politics and current affairs, and the occasional presence of my wife, Jill Chadwick, who has played the part of 'calmer'. All of these people have been a fathomless source of support for me and this book therefore bears their spiritual imprint.

The manuscript was typed and discussed by my true and steadfast friend, Sylvia Greenwood, who knows more about the root soil of this research, in my own paranoid illness in 1979, than either of us would like to declare.

1

WHAT DO WE REALLY MEAN BY 'PARANOIA'?

'Paranoia' is a term that means slightly different things to different people. In this chapter I will be looking at the conditions which have to be present if we say that someone is paranoid and also try to clarify some common misunderstandings.

The critical and essential feature of the paranoid condition is the suspicion that other people are involved in some kind of scheme or plot, however simple or however intricate, against oneself – with the intention to do harm in some way. It is not sufficient, for example, that a person feels simply that they are hated or disliked. Also, merely being afraid, on its own, is not enough for anyone to be said to be paranoid. It is the inference of *planning* and *intent* in others that is the common thread to the thinking and feeling of all genuinely paranoid people.

This importance of intent is critical in distinguishing between complaining people and paranoid people. Both attribute negative events to something outside of themselves. Blaming someone else, however, (as lovers often do when they bicker) may protect one's feelings of self-esteem or self-worth, but if you only blame them for their *stupidity* or carelessness this is obviously not paranoia. Paranoia comes in when you blame someone else's *malign intent*; so, 'She did that *on purpose*'.

Paranoia, like anxiety and fear, is also a feeling, or rather a blend of feelings and thoughts, that is directed towards *the future*. Guilt is directed towards the past while shock and surprise are very much in the present. For these reasons we can feel *hurt* about being disliked, but we are paranoid when thinking that our antagonist is up to something (ahead in time) to discredit us.

Paranoid intelligence

Paranoia is quite a sophisticated mental process, maybe unique to humans. It is not at all a sign of stupidity. It requires anticipation, imagination, empathy and often quite sophisticated inferences and 'second guessing'. For these reasons paranoid people are often highly intelligent and can rise to high places in our society. Paranoid schizophrenics are also generally more intelligent than sufferers of other forms of schizophrenia.[1] This 'power of paranoia', sometimes well-placed, sometimes misplaced, will be seen quite a few times in these pages.

EMPATHY

Paranoia, at its very foundation, requires that a person is able to realize that other people have *minds* that can scheme and intend things. This may not seem to be any great capacity, but it is strangely not possessed by autistic people.[2] Autistics are therefore never genuinely paranoid, although they can be angry or fearful and, in a psychologically rather restricted sense, 'obsessional' or 'phobic'. People who are not autistic but who are very low in *empathy* can also hate or fear people, but generally are not particularly paranoid (or, indeed, neurotic). In a sense they don't have the 'social imagination' to develop this problem. In contrast, paranoid people score very high in empathy (and neuroticism) in questionnaires designed to measure these traits.[3]

Rational paranoia

The fact that a person may think that 'something is going on' or that 'word is getting around' about them doesn't automatically mean that they are just imagining things. We tend to think that a person is paranoid when they're wrong (even though we're not always in a position to be sure they're wrong anyway!). Being paranoid and *correct* is known as 'rational paranoia' (see also Chapter 2 on this). There are plenty of instances of rational paranoia to be found, particularly in countries run by highly authoritarian regimes. It is the common assumption that paranoid people are wrong which leads many individuals to refuse even to listen to others when they talk in this way. It is an omission that isolates the sufferer even more, particularly since it's quite often unfair.[4]

Paranoia, phobias and obsessions

Depending on the certainty of intent in the person's fearful thinking, paranoia can fade back into phobia if the suspicion of intent is weak or barely existent. Therefore, many people who are phobic of social situations are not necessarily paranoid. Also, depending on the degree of preoccupation with the distressing thoughts, paranoia can overlap with obsessions too. So a person can be *phobic* of cats but doesn't generally think that cats are plotting against them; they're not *paranoid* about cats. But a person can be paranoid about a neighbour and if they talk of nothing else they are, sadly, also *obsessed*. So paranoia, phobias and obsessions do tend to form a cluster, depending on the weightings of different processes in a person's mind. We will come across this triangular pattern again later.

Thoughts and feelings

When the person's beliefs and suspicions are unjustified, paranoia is usually regarded as a 'thought disorder'. Conditions such as mania and depression, by contrast, are called 'mood disorders'. This is a very controversial distinction[5] as people may start thinking in a paranoid way as a defence against some mood, say depression, or to give sustenance to a mood or feeling, such as guilt or even hypomania ('less than mania'). The traditional view has been that in paranoids the *thoughts* are abnormal and primary, the feelings (e.g. fear and anger) secondary and due to the malfunctioning in thinking.

I think it would be fair to say that we're not at all sure of this argument any more, at least to the extent that it always applies to paranoia. So in this book I am treating non-rational paranoia as a problem in both thought *and* feeling – with the contributions of each varying in different cases. This seems to me to do justice to the clinical evidence.

Paranoia as a state of mind is a blend of many qualities. It involves apprehension, suspicion, guilt, shame, anger, anxiety and, at times, outright terror. It can induce ruminative thinking, retributive fantasies, sleeplessness, blame, marriage breakdown, litigation, violence, heavy drinking, and sometimes even murder or suicide – or both.

Most readers will be familiar with the harrowing reports in the press and on television etc. of paranoid psychotic and discharged paranoid schizophrenic patients 'at large' in the community; on rare and tragic occasions, killing innocent people under the pressure of delusions and/or hallucinations ('voices' in the head). The cases of the murders committed by patients such as Christopher Clunis and Curtis Howard come to mind. We will see in this book just how these seemingly outrageous and bizarre acts could come about. But for the moment let us find out what the characteristics are of people diagnosed as mentally ill with paranoia. These phenomena may seem a little less terrifying if we have some knowledge about what we are dealing with. People mentally ill with paranoia are *not* in a category apart from normal and 'sane' people, they are part of the human race and they also deserve care and attention – not repulsion and disgust.

Paranoid schizophrenia

Roughly speaking, delusions have been thought of as unshared incredible beliefs, held with high conviction and emotional commitment, and which are impervious to argument and contradiction.[6] They occur in over seventy disorders [7] and are a great source of distress. So common and perplexing are delusions that they have come to be regarded as the central problem of psychopathology.[8] Here I will have to be selective and so I will consider the chief diagnostic categories in which delusions, especially of a paranoid type, feature as highly prominent.[9]

The category that most readers are familiar with is, of course, *paranoid schizophrenia*. This is the most common form of schizophrenia; it is slightly more common in immigrants, who feel alienated and who may not speak the country's language very well, and also in men and in the better educated.[10] It is characterized by organized and systematized delusions, usually of persecution (e.g. being the victim of a plot by aliens or by MI5), but sometimes of grandiosity – these involve elevations in the person's sense of their own importance. Persecutory and grandiose delusions can also co-exist in the same person and indeed some doctors regard them as related phenomena.[11]

The central delusion of paranoid schizophrenic people usually induces them to make all kinds of false inferences about even trivial events going on around them; for example, about something said on the radio or about a sign in a shop window. Sufferers frequently perceive these 'messages' as cryptically referring in some way to *them*. Such false thoughts are referred to as 'ideas of reference' or 'delusions of reference'. So, for example, a sufferer may think that a 'No Smoking' sign has been deliberately put in a particular place that day (again by MI5 or the secret police etc.) so that they would see it, with the aim of stopping them smoking. All manner of trivial phenomena can be misinterpreted in this way, so that it is not possible to be sure how a paranoid schizophrenic person's delusions are going to develop or influence their behaviour. A lot of strange or even violent acts by such people are due to them over-reacting to trivia of these kinds in public places (see Chapter 3 on this).

The person usually suffers from auditory hallucinations – voices commenting on their behaviour, arguing between themselves and echoing their thoughts. These voices may also unpredictably induce them to commit violent or antisocial acts or, indeed, to injure or even kill themselves.

When these symptoms are upon them, sufferers of paranoid schizophrenia are not surprisingly extremely distressed, angry, irritable and, at times, violent. Although they are not as well organized in behaviour as non-psychotic people, nonetheless they're relatively coherent and their emotional life is (generally, at least) along the lines that one would expect, given the way they think. Their behaviour, although striking, is to some degree 'understandable' *if* one accepts their delusion as true. If a person has delusions but their behaviour is grossly incoherent and disorganized, their form of schizophrenia is, by definition, not of the paranoid type.

The schizophrenia label, for better or worse, is applied for example, if the person has shown signs of severe disturbance in their social and occupational functioning, and self-care, for at least *six months* and delusions and hallucinations (psychotic symptoms) have been present for at least a month. Alternatively, at another extreme, the person may *not* have slowly deteriorated in social functioning etc. but they *have* shown psychotic symptoms for about six months. Either way, a doctor is looking for signs of illness in the person for about half a year. In some people, the build-up to actual symptoms (the so-called 'active phase') is gradual; in others, the symptoms come on distressingly suddenly, with little warning for friends and relatives (the latter is often due to a recent shock such as a break-up with a partner or the death of a parent they were close to).

Paranoid disorder

In cases where hallucinations are not prominent, and if the person's behaviour is well organized, less odd and their general level of functioning in life is less deteriorated than in schizophrenia, a deluded person may receive the diagnosis of *delusional disorder* or *paranoid disorder*. The delusions here can be quite varied. They may be of jealousy, persecution, a fear of having some terrible disease, a feeling that a famous person is in love with them, or that they are a great and exalted individual, perhaps related to a major historical figure – or that they have special powers and capacities.

Brief reactive psychosis

Delusions of a paranoid type can also commonly occur in a person with a less serious psychotic disorder called *brief reactive psychosis* or *brief psychotic disorder*. This occurs when an individual becomes ill under a stress that would be likely to upset anyone in the same circumstances and the episode is quite brief, perhaps only a day or so up to a month. Sufferers are usually in great turmoil and confusion, the stresses being what they are, but they return to full functioning quite quickly. A hypothetical case of paranoid illness which I give in Chapter 3 is really best described as a brief reactive psychosis. In clinical terms the sufferer is, thankfully, not very ill even though their thoughts seem superficially to be disturbing and strange.

Paranoid personality disorder

The three categories I've mentioned above (paranoid schizophrenia, paranoid disorder and brief reactive psychosis) are all types of psychotic illness, what in everyday life we refer to as 'madness'. The person is totally unable to discriminate fantasy from reality and they have little or no insight into the fact that their beliefs and fears are without foundation. Indeed they take their fantasies to *be* reality, whatever they are, and may become extremely irritable or cantankerous if the truth of their beliefs is severely questioned – especially if someone adopts a confrontative style with them.

However, another group of problems that clinical psychologists and psychiatrists frequently meet is that of *personality disorders*. People with personality disorders are not mad. In this form of mental pathology the person does not manifest their abnormality in *symptoms*, such as hallucinations and delusions, but in *the kind of person they are*.[12] The psychotic person has dysfunctional symptoms; the personality-disordered person has dysfunctional traits. In the former we speak of a 'personality with a problem', in the latter of a 'problem personality'.

One of the categories of personality disorder is, predictably, the *paranoid personality disorder*. Such people have generally been like this since their late teenage or early adult years. They have a very suspicious and cynical attitude and are forever interpreting people's actions as involving trickery, deception, malice, fraudulent intent or, in general, some manoeuvre to 'get around them' etc. (They are also always quick to tell you how they are 'usually right', even when there is no way of establishing whether their inferences are right or wrong anyway.)

People with a paranoid personality disorder are always bearing grudges; they fear confiding in others in case the information they disclose is used against them and they are very quick to take offence. Generally they take criticism extremely badly, over-react to contradiction and are forever questioning their partner's fidelity (if they are lucky enough to have a partner). Their lives are peppered with 'mini-delusions' which rise and fall in their minds as they bump and bounce their way through life's problems and challenges; and they are *incapable* of ever being happy or of maintaining a lasting relationship with anyone. One of their favourite activities is not love but litigation.

Such people have sufficient grasp of reality to function independently and with a modicum of efficiency. They are rarely seen in the clinic or consulting room except, say, as

interfering spouses or parents, because they are so confident
that there is nothing wrong with them that they never ask
anyone in the mental health sphere for help. They come to
the attention of doctors sometimes after minor breaches of
the law, when they are referred for reports, or when their
marriage is collapsing and they deign to turn up for marriage
guidance – if only to blame everything on their spouse.

People like this are often highly intelligent and verbally
skilful to the extent that they are always able to convince
themselves, if nobody else, of their utter innocence in all
matters involving interpersonal friction.

'Manic paranoia'

The word 'maniac', which obviously derives from the condition of mania, describes behaviour characteristic of the 'mad'
for many people. Individuals who suffer from mania generally have immense energy and highly inflated ideas about
themselves, they are extremely talkative and distract-ible,
need little sleep and are wildly over-confident of the success
of everything they venture into. On the inside they have the
experience that their thoughts are racing ('tachyphrenia') and
they continually involve themselves in activities which will
give them the mental 'high' that they crave. The negative
side of this disorder is the frequent ruin of their relationships
or marriage, the collapse of their ventures, massive over-
spending and bankruptcy and, often, a reversal of mood into
bottomless black depression – the latter being characteristic
of so-called 'bipolar affective disorder'.

Mania and paranoia have frequently been linked in the
psychological and psychoanalytic literature. In both types
there is elevation of self-esteem (paranoids often also have
grandiose ideas about themselves), an enhancement of mental

speed if not accuracy, general over-confidence in judgment, a spectacular larger-than-life quality to the thoughts and behaviour of both groups of people. Some clinicians have regarded the two conditions as not intrinsically separable, arguing that at a process level they stem from identical mental operations. Clearly, there are many similarities. The thinking of paranoid patients is often suspiciously manic in flavour, to the extent that one wonders why they have not taken to thriller writing (as of course some do) rather than 'patienthood'.

People diagnosed as essentially manic but 'severely manic' also have delusions and/or hallucinations. These may be 'congruent' with the mood, as when a person thinks they are a Messiah, or 'incongruent' when the thoughts are persecutory (even though their mood is positive).[13]

It is interesting for theories of paranoia which infer a motivated escape from *depression* being involved that mania too has long been seen to have this function.

'Depressive paranoia'

One of the paradoxes of mental disturbance is that the very thing a person is trying to avoid may yet return as a secondary consequence of their psychic manouevres. Paranoid thinking, even if it is initially exciting, eventually becomes tormenting and usually induces depression as an accompanying mood. Few sufferers of paranoia I have met are free from melancholy feelings, and melancholy feelings can even in themselves breed a further strata of paranoia: as when one woman said to me, 'I worry so much, I'm sure everyone knows I'm a misery and hates me for it'. Clearly, paranoid thoughts and malfunctions of mood are intricately related.

Paranoia in schizoaffective psychosis

Schizoaffective disorder is a highly controversial category, which includes people who have both the active psychotic features of schizophrenia *and* a major manic or depressive syndrome. The reader can probably guess that disturbances of perception, thought and feeling so frequently go together in people that this is, at worst, a 'catch-all' diagnosis and at best the most fundamental and fair psychosis diagnosis of all.

Folie à deux

If a person lives in a close relationship with a paranoid person, it is not remarkable for them to share some of their partner's beliefs. When this process reaches the level where the person truly does believe and share their partner's delusion with comparable conviction it is known as 'shared paranoid disorder' or 'induced psychotic disorder', more commonly referred to as 'Folie à deux'. The delusion is said to be induced because the co-sufferer was symptom-free and not showing any 'build-up' signs of schizophrenia or psychosis prior to exposure to their partner's belief. In rare cases *two* people may share an inducing person's ideas; not surprisingly this is referred to as 'Folie à trois'. If *dozens* of people share their beliefs they're usually thought of as a prophet rather than a lunatic! This, of course, illustrates rather poignantly that whether a person is deluded or not is, in the end, a *social* judgement (with all the changes of circumstance that that implies); we do not decide this on the basis, say, of a blood test or a brain scan and it is doubtful that we ever will, or indeed should.

Drugs, ageing and deafness

The group of disorders discussed above are all due to factors which are taken, rightly or wrongly, to be intrinsic to the sufferer – that is, they are not a result of external or extrinsic toxic agents, such as alcohol or cannabis. It is important to realize, however, that fast-developing (and usually brief) paranoid delusions do occur in some people regularly using the following drugs: cocaine, PCP (phencyclidine), cannabis, amphetamines, alcohol, LSD and other hallucinogens. Even carbon monoxide, insecticides, carbon dioxide and fuel and paint have been known to induce psychotic symptoms.

Substance-related disorders are more commonly diagnosed in males and in those aged about 18 to 24; but there are wide cultural and sex-ratio variations. The disorder occurs either during intoxication with the substance (with cocaine this can occur in minutes) or it can occur during withdrawal – even up to four weeks after the person has stopped using the drug. Withdrawal symptoms are particularly unpleasant with alcohol, in alcohol-dependent people. Symptoms due to a drug may also persist for weeks or even longer after its cessation – especially in the cases of amphetamine, phencyclidine and cocaine.

Psychosis almost indistinguishable from paranoid schizophrenia can develop quickly with amphetamine use. Apart from delusions, auditory hallucinations and distortions of the body image, users may also think that bugs or insects are crawling in or under their skin. Persecutory delusions associated with great anxiety, volatile emotions and amnesia for the episode are occasionally linked to cannabis use; although the episodes are usually very brief. Long-term use of cannabis can be associated with the evocation of a paranoid disposition in some people and cases of paranoia produced by regular use of the drug Ecstasy (E) have been reported.

Testosterone boosters taken, for example to improve performance at sport, can induce both paranoia and mania.[14] Paranoia may also occur in the deaf or partly deaf,[15] in many neurological and metabolic disorders and in schizophrenia (and depression) in the elderly.

As an aside it is also true that people who suffer greatly and centrally from anxiety, and are essentially of a neurotic rather than psychotic disposition, may have or develop various short-lived paranoid fears around many areas of their lives; but these do not usually crystallize into an overriding singular paranoid conviction.

———————

The groupings described above are obviously not exhaustive, but they probably cover most of the territory that clinicians experience. It is important to recognize, however, that in real life, these categories are not truly discrete. Every person is an individual. In truth, no-one can be 'typed', all categories fade into one another and in real life practice we deal not so much with distinct patterns but rather 'exceptions'. Even those whose paranoia is drug-induced are usually psychologically or physiologically vulnerable in some way, as not all drug users suffer these symptoms. The drug or drug combination does not simply put paranoia in their minds as if by 'chemical magic' it releases something dormant within, at least in part – particularly as a function also of their current mood or situation. But in the same way life, and the stresses of life, can release something latent within us all at different times, we all have our own unique way of malfunctioning. Paranoia is the choice of some, even in madness; but they are no less human for that.

2

WHAT CAUSES PARANOIA?
A BIRD'S-EYE VIEW

People often joke about paranoia, saying: 'the fact that you're paranoid doesn't mean that they're not still out to get you' and 'if you're not a bit paranoid – you're crazy'. Such 'common-sense' intuitions reflect two important aspects of the disorder that psychologists consider important. First, people are rarely paranoid for no good reason; and secondly, paranoia, or at least a mild degree of it, can be a useful, self-protective attitude of mind in a hostile world. Few people can avoid feeling fearful and possibly paranoid when someone unexpectedly rings their doorbell at 1 a.m.

Carl Sagan[1] recounts a disturbing anecdote about the first U.S. Secretary of Defence, James Forrestal. Forrestal, diagnosed as paranoid by physicians, plunged to his death from an upper store of the Walter Reed Army Hospital, convinced that Israeli secret agents were following him everywhere. Eventually it transpired that Israeli agents *had* been following him because they were worried that he might come to a secret understanding with representatives of Arab nations. Forrestal's 'delusions' did go beyond the actual reality to some degree, but his anguish at being hospitalized and labelled psychotic for believing something that was essentially true, must have been indescribable, and undoubtedly weakened his sanity even further.

A young Pakistani man, Shafiq, who I was friendly with in the early 1980s, similarly had the belief that people in Fulham, West London, were monitoring him, talking about him and often saying, 'That's him' to each other on seeing him in the street. Shafiq had so many other beliefs that seemed absurd (such as that Americans believed him to be 'the greatest man in the world') that most people who knew him dismissed these latest worries as delusional. One evening I went with Shafiq and some other friends to a pub in Fulham and while I was away at the bar getting the drinks, a man had apparently leaned around the enclosure where he was sitting, seen Shafiq, and said to his friend, 'It's him!' Everyone present heard this; it was no hallucination. Shafiq, rather than being mortified, was instead quite delighted by this event. It proved to all that his grasp on reality, which to us all is so vital, was at least to some degree sound.

There is, indeed, nothing worse for a paranoid patient than a well-meaning psychiatrist rejecting every suspicious judgement about reality they make in the altruistic interest of making them worry less! Its effect is to pitch them into a no-win situation and make them feel that their anchoring in the world is so tenuous and slippery that they have to deny even self-evident truth.

Because the world can be dangerous, and always has been, this makes paranoia both inevitable and also very useful. If it wasn't useful, the attitude would probably have disappeared over the aeons of time during which humans have evolved. If you *anticipate* danger, work out what's going on, and avoid it, you live to fight another day. In a sense, paranoid thinking is quite normal. But it's also the inevitable outcome of the existence of society itself. Society requires a certain degree of conformity and standardization in people's behaviour and appearance for its very 'cement'. If a person is different in some way, or in many ways that are not at all fashionable, they're a threat to the group and so they're bound to be scrutinized, talked about and maybe even plotted against – basically in order to bring them 'into line' or, failing this, to label them as an outcast to be shunned (and, in terms of the animal kingdom, maybe not mated with). While there is society there will always be paranoia. The only way to be sure of avoiding it is to be both a complete mediocrity and to *enjoy* being a complete mediocrity. Then no-one picks on you.

'Many roads to Rome'

Given that we all have a basic and valuable *capacity* for paranoia, it is not surprising that paranoia can be triggered off in diverse ways. We have to realize that there are, as the saying goes, many roads to Rome. This is what psychologists call 'equifinality' – the existence of many routes to the same kind of mental state.

To get a taste of this, and to take the most obvious possibility first, a paranoid attitude to the world can be learned (or rather brought out) in the early years of life by the way our parents behave and the way they talk. A parent who is always implying how deceitful and untrustworthy other people are, or who continually interprets bad events, even if they were only accidents, as *intended* by malevolent others, is going to insinuate that kind of thinking gradually into their children's minds. Paranoid thinking will become 'salient' or rather *stand out* to the child; just as, over the years, food consciousness and weight consciousness can be made by some parents (and the media) to stand out in the mind of the budding anorexic girl. It becomes 'significant', 'the way to think'. In psychological terms it becomes a 'dominant' attitude or feeling, around which other thoughts and feelings become organized.

We have to be careful here to distinguish between paranoia that's appropriate ('rational paranoia') and that which is inappropriate. Some neighbourhoods, for example, have very little community spirit. People may be competitive, relatively isolated in their own family home and just out for what they can get. Others may be very poor and so, unable to survive by legitimate means, people use their only assets – their wits and cunning – to get by. In 'communities' like this, where really there is no community, paranoid influences may not be false alarms at all but perfectly correct. (In psychological terms we can distinguish here between 'false alarms' and so-called 'hits'. The latter are decisions about reality that really do match with it.)

The nature of the community is a far from trivial matter. The quality of community life depends not only on the residents but on a wide range of people, from government ministers to local authority officials, architects, planners and designers and also police working in the area of crime prevention. People in neighbourhoods with a real sense of community are more mutually supportive, and paranoid attitudes have less chance of getting a hold.

Therefore, although it might be thought that we are dealing here with a topic that is definitely the province only of the psychologist and psychiatrist, this is by no means entirely so. Society may inevitably breed paranoia, but it can also go some way to alleviating it if people really care about each other. Not surprisingly, such measures as the building of community centres, day centres for children and youth clubs, which all bring people together, give opportunities for mutual activity and bonding one to another, which works against the isolation and fear that so easily pushes people into thinking in a morbid way. It decreases crime rates as well. Paranoia is not only an individual thing; it's also the price of a society with no sense of community — so it is necessary to be careful not to fall into the easy trap of 'blaming the victim'.[2]

PEOPLE WHO ARE DIFFERENT

When people are paranoid for *no* good reason, psychologists refer to their inferences as 'false alarms'. With regard to people who are noticeably different from the majority in the culture, such as immigrants, homosexuals, lesbians, people who are extremely physically unattractive and so on, it becomes very difficult to separate 'hits' from false alarms in the things that they say.

Some people, such as homosexuals and transvestites, however, have eased their paranoid pressure to some degree not by therapy or pills but by community action. They have created their own subculture, particularly over the past thirty years or so (clubs, discos and so on), where they can be more at ease. But they may still be stigmatized and discriminated against at work, where they are forced to fit in with people from the dominant group. In America 'ugly' people have taken the same route and there are some clubs and societies specifically created by themselves for themselves; while others have solved their paranoia in a different way, not by psychotherapy but by cosmetic surgery. But for still others the smirks of 'normals' remain and, as often as not, are real.

The problem for psychologists trying to help paranoia sufferers is that we human beings have a tremendous capacity for 'going beyond the information given'. We don't just respond or react to stimuli; we infer, guess, anticipate and expect. In so many ways our imagination *adds* to reality. But if we didn't we would have no theatres, no bridges, no journeys to the moon, as well as no paranoid disorders.

The imaginative paranoid

Paranoid people are often highly creative and imaginative (and also extremely rational), at least in paranoid directions. This may seem surprising but if some of the paranoid people I have met had turned their undoubted gifts to writing novels of real intrigue, short stories or disturbing screenplays, they might have been highly successful. (The writer Philip K. Dick would be an example of this.) Instead, they simply wrapped their lives up inside their own heads and became ineffectually obsessed with their own private fantasies — fantasies usually only shared with psychiatrists. Paranoia can be a terrible waste of talent.

Others have been more fortunate, turning their paranoid disposition to something generally regarded as socially legitimate, such as becoming Social Security fraud investigators or private detectives, continually spying on straying spouses. Sometimes a paranoid style of thinking can actually get you a living wage!

The human imagination cannot be quelled (although in Victorian times some teachers did try) and in the last analysis we wouldn't really have it any other way. But one negative consequence of spectacular imaginings is real paranoid *disorder*: where the person's fantastic fantasies are just that, and are causing them, and everybody else, far more harm than good. While admitting that paranoia rarely rests on a basis of thin air, how is it that it can go beyond, and in madness so *far* beyond, any semblance of a match with reality?

You may well guess here, and rightly, that this is only going to be possible in three ways. First, the way the person has been brought up has been *appropriate* to that family and general situation but it is way out of touch with the culture or general scene that they now live in – so that they are continually misinterpreting what goes on around them ('developmental explanation'). Secondly, their upbringing and general environment has been quite normal for the culture but there is something about *them*, something *internal* to them, be it genetic or motivational etc., which grossly biases their inferences, ('internal explanation'). *Or*, thirdly, some combination of these two.

I have met people who represent every gradation or interaction between these two extreme explanations, and also some who do actually fall at those extremes. Let us take the *internal* explanation first and then move on to the ways a person can be biased, relatively speaking, by external or family influences. As this is a summary chapter, I will deal with the processes concerned only in outline here; but more detailed analyses can be found later in the book.

'PROJECTION'
Until about 1974, paranoid disorder was considered by psychologists, and particularly psychoanalysts, to be due to a defensive process called 'projection'. This is the tendency to attribute to others feelings which are unacceptable to oneself, that one does nevertheless entertain unconsciously. So instead of facing the fact that you *hate* people, you defend against this by saying, 'It is not I who hate, it is people who hate me'. The unacceptable emotion is 'projected' out of the self and into others, leaving the individual innocent of the negative impulse. Hence Freud was able to say that, 'the price of innocence is delusional'.

Many therapists find this theory intuitively plausible. After all, most individuals (though perhaps not all) prefer to deal with an external danger than with one that is internal. The problem, however, is that the actual objective evidence for the theory is at best ambiguous [3,4] and there are many people in clinical practice for whom it seems totally inappropriate. Another difficulty is that if this model is clung to and evidence is searched for to fit it, that evidence will be found regardless – something that the client also has a tendency to do when they scan the world to find evidence that fits their cherished delusional thoughts. So the therapist can end up in the same kind of self-confirming fantasy roundabout as the person they are trying to help. This gets nobody anywhere. Although it is plausible that this kind of process applies to *some* individuals, it is far better to have a range of possibilities available to apply to every specific case – and be prepared to jettison them all and create new ones if they all turn out to be wrong.

ABNORMAL EXPERIENCES

In more recent times many other routes to paranoia have been discovered. Now Freud's early formulation,[5] which seeded paranoia partly in the rejection of homosexual impulses (i.e. 'I, a man, do not love him, I hate him – No! I don't hate him, he hates me') has not been found even by psychoanalysts to be true for women[6]; and now some psychoanalysts reject the general projection approach as a panacea.[7] A less mentally acrobatic process was suggested by Maher[8] and this certainly finds objective confirmation.

Maher argued that the thought processes of paranoid people are quite normal but that the sensory *evidence*, the basic 'roughage' on which the thought processes go to work, is what is abnormal. This theory has excellent application, for example, in people who are partially deaf. When auditory information is not clear it is very easy indeed to think that people are 'whispering' and from this to deduce that they may be scheming or plotting. Because of this, paranoia can be temporarily induced in normal people in whom partial deafness has also been experimentally induced.⁹

It is also possible to imagine, working along these lines, that paranoia could develop from something simply *misheard* but of a seemingly ominous quality. Theorizing such as this is obviously less spectacular than Freud's, but there definitely are people who have become paranoid in just this way. In the case of people who suffer auditory hallucinations, the development of consequent paranoid ideas, derived from the voices they have heard, is a very clear example of Maher's theory.

The Maher approach dominated the thinking of psychologists, especially in the USA, throughout the 1980s, while the Freudian emphasis tended to fade. However, we now have good reason to believe that paranoid people *do* often have abnormal thought processes as well as perceptual problems, and investigations to prise out these abnormalities have accelerated since then. The general flavour of Freud's approach, that is, his inference that paranoid thinking is in some way *defensive* and *motivated*, is also coming back into vogue, although in slightly different form.

PARANOIA, MANIA AND DEPRESSION

A paranoid person usually feels that *other people* are to blame for their distress or for the mess their life is in etc. In contrast, depressed people have a strong tendency in the other direction. They blame *themselves* for all their misfortunes. This has led to the realization that, in some cases, paranoia is a defence against depression; the person is shifting control and responsibility for their bad life situation from inside themselves to outside. What is happening here is that the person is shifting *responsibility* outwards rather than, say, unconscious anger.[10,11,12] However, the effect of this is often to make them very angry people! Not surprisingly, many systems of paranoid thought are rather manic in flavour too — and mania has long been seen as, in part, an escape from depression.

GUILT

Were we to speak to the proverbial passenger on the Clapham omnibus about this it's very likely that he would remind us of the the importance of a guilty conscience. The guilty person, after all, feels that they deserve to be betrayed, punished, 'shown up' for what they really are — be it a trickster, a poseur, a murderer or whatever. In psychoanalytic theory, whether the person is defending against homosexual impulses or against inner unacknowledged rage,[13] it is guilt that is the reason for the repressing force. But, of course, there are plenty of people who have become paranoid because of guilt they consciously feel, rather than out of the need cryptically to avoid an *unconscious* feeling.

Freud was nonetheless right to see sexual guilt as important in generating paranoia. Sex being the impulse still surrounded by most taboos and most ignorance, there are many individuals with sexual problems or variations, from impotence and fetishism to sado-masochism and paedophilia, who can barely live with their impulses and become hopelessly paranoid at the slightest hint that their peculiarity has been discovered by 'outsiders'. Very few people with sexual problems (variants) are 'monsters' parading their inclinations for all to see and indoctrinating little boys into perverse ways. The majority, particularly those with intolerant partners, or whose practices are illegal or the subject of mockery and ridicule, may have to build in their minds whole 'philosophies' of conduct around their desires – in which their needs sit as perfectly legitimate – as a way of countering paranoia and intolerable shame. In this way, however, paranoia – rather than being simply a source of anguish – can actually act as a spur to the justification of acts that were previously seen as strange and misunderstood by the public. This has happened in the twentieth century with many sexual practices, from masturbation to transvestism.

Psychologists speak of 'a negative reinforcer' as something which makes you act in a particular way to avoid it. It is different from 'punishment', which merely stops you in your tracks. Where the elimination of the shame and guilt surrounding sex is concerned, it's clear that paranoia has been a tremendously powerful negative reinforcer for the human intellect. It is another of the many 'uses' of paranoia.

SHAME

Shame and guilt are obviously related and both are highly evident in paranoia. Guilt is perhaps more to do with the way we look in our *own* eyes when we've violated our own standards; shame is more to do with how we look in the eyes of *others* when we have violated the standards of our culture.[14] One way to triumph over shame, which we can probably all recognize in our own lives, is via a 'don't care' or 'bloody-minded' attitude, in which we 'damn the eyes' of the staring, shaming mob. But another technique is to blame something or someone external to ourselves for the very failings which have caused our shame. People in politics and sport can often be seen to do this because they are so much in the public eye. Here, shame, as a negative reinforcer, *motivates* a paranoid attitude rather than accompanying it[15] and results in a reduction in the shame that we feel. Various bleatings such as, 'It's the umpire's fault', 'It's the fault of the previous administration', 'The press are to blame', 'It's all due to Major and Clarke' and so on, testify to the massive use of paranoia itself, from mild to severe, as a defence against shame.[16]

Paranoid jealousy

When we love someone it's natural for us to want them for ourselves – some degree of jealousy is inevitable because our love does make us dependent. Indeed a certain amount of jealousy is a useful signal that someone *does* care and in men may be a way of 'keeping the female' and preserving one's genes in the face of competing males. A partner may worry (usually with reason) if their lover is not jealous in the slightest. Alas, paranoid jealousy, where there is possessiveness, suspicion and accusation to a bizarre degree, completely ruins thousands of relationships. In some Mediterranean countries the attitude may be partly learned as 'the way men behave'. For Latin lovers 'paranoid' jealousy is virtually a stereotyped behaviour and a culturally agreed sign of passion and commitment (as well as a 'legitimate' method of subjugating women). But in cooler Northern Europeans it takes on a slightly different significance, as it does not fit any behavioural cliché. It is generally a sign that something *specific* is definitely wrong. What could cause paranoid jealousy when there *really is* no basis for it?

Some people who are so jealous that they badly damage their affairs feel deep down that their relationships with the opposite sex hang only by a mere cotton thread (and may well have good reason for thinking this). They may even be *surprised* that they have managed to attract the partner that they have – and they secretly expect that cotton thread to break at any moment. Their jealousy reaches obsessive paranoid proportions because they secretly *need* their paranoid thoughts – they *have* to be right. The way they have seen people and the world, the way they have made sense out of it has, after all, served them well in the past through countless experiences. If a person cannot judge *reality* accurately what have they got?! Implicitly, this is inwardly what they are saying to themselves. Their inference *must* be right because, if it isn't, their whole model of existence will fall apart. This is the 'paranoia paradox': they are prepared to risk, and even allow to happen, the ruin of their relationship rather than radically change that model of reality. To be right is logically more important than being good or even loved.

Because of the assumption that their bond with their partner is cotton-thin even the *slightest* evidence will be taken to confirm this, such as a warm smile to another man or woman, or an extra-long handshake. Living with people like this can be a tormenting experience and their insight into their exasperating behaviour is usually pretty minimal. The longing to be right coupled with the terror of anticipated loss are both so great that consciousness is filled and clouded by the intensity of the feelings and the anguish of the conflict.

A motive that may co-exist with the assumption of threadbare bonding is the fear that without their beloved they will also simply 'implode' and wither away. Other people, for example men with utterly devoted mothers, are embittered by the rockier coastlines of relationships with other women, where the total unconditional love a mother gives her child is simply not to be found.

So great is the need of the paranoidly jealous to *possess* their partner totally that the slightest risk to the status quo is taken as a mortal threat. Such people have very little capacity to exist as independent, autonomous individuals. They live *through* their partners: in pretending to give life to them, in reality they suck life out of them.

Paranoid jealousy always masquerades as deep and devoted love, whereas in fact it is founded on weakness, insecurity, deep dependency and inadequacy – blended with hatred. It is hatred at their partner for their imagined infidelity and for 'causing' their dependency; hatred at the world and at themselves for their own weakness; and hatred even at the future for the separation it might at any moment bring.

This brief account of paranoid jealousy is obviously hardly exhaustive – but the theme of inner inadequacy and dependency is always present. A man may, for example, ferociously cling to a woman if he sees her as 'the solution' to his own sexual problems or inadequacy – once she is gone he may fear relapse into being a masturbating loner, a reject or a sexual pervert. 'She *must* be *all mine*' is his desperate motto. Or he may, as Freud suggested,[5] defensively fear the attraction of 'his woman' to a man that really he secretly desires himself: 'I do not love him, *she* does!'.

A range of motivational patterns, that one can only discover by conversation, present themselves underpinning this state. A *conscious* form of projection, such as 'Just as I desire others – so does he' can coexist with suppressed anger, 'I hate him for indulging himself in the forbidden when I have not'. Every such case has to be faced as a new challenge and a range of possibilities considered. The paranoidly jealous *can* be helped. Although paranoid people are generally thought to have no insight at all into their condition this is not necessarily so – but the jealous do fit this stereotype distressingly well. Few will therefore read this book, but perhaps their partners will.

Grandiosity and paranoia

When basically ordinary people start saying that MI5 or the CIA are spying on them, or that they're 'the talk of the town' and such like, it's difficult to avoid the inference that this kind of paranoia actually gives them some subtle pleasure: after all, anyone who is the subject of so much attention must surely be a person of consequence. 'Paranoid fame' usually strikes people who, in truth, really feel very insignificant and, sadly, of no consequence at all. The pain of paranoid fame is the price they pay for the cryptic pleasure of at least being well-known for *something*.

Paranoid fame produces a surge of feeling of personal potency and personal relevance to the world. The victim is in 'the centre', now no longer a speck or an outsider but a focus, very much in-the-world and the apex of all the action. In this way, paranoia can give the individual the rather grandiose illusion of being an important part of ongoing reality; a feeling is thus induced in someone who previously felt a total outcast, of no real use or relevance to life at all.

Rather than face the hard slog of actually contributing to the world in an important and useful way, something that could take decades, this form of paranoia results from the person instead taking the easy short-cut of making a leap of somewhat manic quality, a leap in their imagination, from the periphery of life right into the centre. People who make hoax calls to the police, claiming that there is 'a bomb at Victoria Station', etc. and therefore, with minimal effort, totally disrupt the day of millions of London commuters and thousands of businesses, also make use of this kind of easy solution, the periphery-to-centre leap, so as to assuage their basic feelings of being utter, and usually bored, non-entities.

The existence of the modern news media makes this kind

of easy fame possible, and many an inadequate criminal has
made use of the massive communication networks that we
have to 'flash' their identity to millions, if only for a few
seconds or minutes; to thus prove to themselves and to
everybody else that they do, after all, exist and can make *an
impact*.

The mental processes involved in paranoid fame are thus
shared by some people who we would not actually regard as
psychotic or mad. However, the paranoid person (and crimi-
nals who are caught) are short-sighted in their use of this
solution to their feelings of low self-esteem. This is another
'paranoia paradox' – that the very solution to their inner
anguish actually, in the long run, causes even more anguish
than they initially felt. Their 'victory' is pyrrhic. Although
they are now at the centre of attention, the situation they
find themselves in is, or can be, a totally unliveable one.
Tormented, persecuted and hated by all, many paranoids find
their only release is in suicide. The 'centre' turned out to be
a black hole, a whirlpool, down which they disappeared into
oblivion; their journey was from nowhere into nothingness.

Paranoid misfits

At this point I will move from looking exclusively at factors
which are internal to the individual and briefly consider how
paranoia can result from a kind of 'misfit' effect. This is
where the way a person has been brought up can so bias their
thinking that they grossly misinterpret a basically benign
reality in paranoid ways.

Early in this chapter I commented on the obvious possibility of direct 'training' in paranoid thinking at home. But
this is not the only way in which this attitude of mind can be
seeded. There are some people who have a terrible 'down'

on the world but whose attitude is more of a *disappointment* than a copied or learned attitude, or an objective statement about life. Pampered by doting parents into feeling blissfully wonderful and special, 'Mummy's darling', 'Daddy's favourite girl' etc. they are shocked and embittered when reality outside the family does not confirm the expectations and opinions of themselves which they were reared to hold. They simply cannot *believe* it when they are laughed at, or hit, or betrayed, or ferociously criticized, and they come to see the world as a far more horrific and hostile place than it generally is.

It is possible to see how this relates to the phenomenon of paranoid fame discussed in the last section. If the notion occurred that there was a district-wide persecutory network, intent on an individual's ridicule and destruction, most people would counter it with the thoughts: a) 'I'm not that important', b) 'I don't deserve it', and c) 'People wouldn't go to all that trouble on account of me'. The pampered paranoid, however, thinks that they *are* that important and that people *would* go to 'all that trouble' on account of them! This is the great danger, first recognized by Alfred Adler, of giving someone experiences which lead to the overvaluation of the self. Here the overvaluation is direct, rather than being due to compensation for inadequacy feelings, but either extreme can lead to the same outcome. Indeed, people ridiculed for their bumptiousness and vanity can pass from one extreme to the other as they get older *and* feel guilty for that past bumptiousness in the process.

A particularly dangerous combination of parental attitudes is that of overprotectiveness and over-involvement, coupled with a great deal of hostility and criticism.[17] This has been demonstrated to be a potent cause of *relapse* in patients suffering from schizophrenia when they return home from hospital [18] but it has also been suggested[19] that these attitudes could well cause mental derangement in the first place, especially in offspring who are genetically vulnerable. The combination of stresses is referred to as 'Expressed emotion' or 'EE' for short. It is easy to see how overprotectiveness could reduce a person's sense of inner strength and autonomy ('without me you're nothing') while criticism of behaviour that the person enacts of their own volition would reinforce their belief in their own ineptitude for the task of life ('everything about you is *wrong*'). Psychological survival in such an environment is a tough assignment and it is likely that feelings of transparency, vulnerability to life, mistrust of self and others and personal inadequacy could be easily induced by parents with this style of behaviour – as indeed they are.

CATASTROPHIC THINKING

The spectacular quality of a lot of paranoid imaginings not only derives from 'good imagination', in the sense of a genetically pre-wired gift and/or a cultivated talent, but also from the tendency in some families to encourage 'over-reaction'; what psychologists call 'catastrophic thinking'. Anorexics and anxiety patients show this bias in their style of thought ('One tuna fish sandwich and I'm finished for life') but paranoid people also demonstrate it ('One mistake and I'll be the talk of the street', 'If people find out my son's been fined my whole life is ruined, I'll never be able to face anyone again' or 'If this gets out suicide is all that's left'). To a catastrophizer everything must be larger than life and every disaster a mega-disaster. Catastrophic thinking is a rather manic failure to face the mundane reality that much of life takes place in the middle ground, that most dreams *don't* come true, that the worst usually *doesn't* happen and that most of us live very average lives and are sadly forgotten a few years after we die. The catastrophizer pays for their need for their life to be like a Hollywood screenplay by continual torment in reaction to what are often very average adversities.

'CONFIRMATION BIAS'

I will talk more about family and environmental influences later in the book, but finally in this chapter I would like to draw attention to the way a particular mental process can be encouraged in children: a process that both has great advantages but also, in paranoia, very great disadvantages. This is what psychologists refer to as 'confirmation bias'.[20,21] This is a bias that really characterizes everyone, but in some people is very extreme. It is a bias to seek and accept data and arguments that *confirm* one's point of view at the expense of any data and arguments that refute or disconfirm it. The bias tends to characterize more creative people[12] but in paranoia it runs riot. Paranoid people are forever 'processing' what goes on around them, whether it is a couple laughing in a pub, the hoot of a car horn, even sometimes an item in the press, as all in some way related to them and their preoccupation or directed at them. This bias also amplifies their belief that 'everybody is against me', because how else could all these events *be* felt to be 'relevant' if this was not so? Although the paranoid is motivated to make the 'leap to the centre' that I spoke of earlier, their cognitive or intellectual apparatus works rather like a slave system to deliver the necessary impressions in their mind that justify that leap. The kind of loose thinking that facilitates confirmation bias also aids creativity – which relies on seeing remote connections and relationships – and the encouragement of this style of thought at home often therefore pays off in creative life. The negative side of the coin, however, is that if the *content* that the person is thinking about changes from life enhancing to self destructive, this bias will take them fast along the latter path too.

———————

As can be imagined, most cases of paranoia involve an interaction of many factors. There are internal factors — genetic, physiological, cognitive and motivational; external ones — real evidence, family influences, community attitudes, and so on; and every permutation of these. The job of the clinician is to discover the pattern of factors that apply in the *individual* case. Studies of large groups of people can only give us general guidelines; at the individual level very specific factors unique to that person may be at work. I have presented the causes of paranoia here in rather a negative light, as if it is always and only a human *failing*. However, paranoid states can also be based on truth: they can have their uses, they can tell us much about the nature of our community, and are often a symptom of that community's failings; and they can reflect great creative and imaginative capacities in the persons who suffer from them. One of the great tragedies of paranoia is that it is so often such an unproductive result of what are basically quite normal — and sometimes even exceptional — mental skills.

3

A RAPID RIDE THROUGH A PSYCHOTIC DELUSION

Most people have a great deal of difficulty getting inside the mind of a gravely paranoid person – particularly when that person is so disturbed as to be reasonably considered insane. How does their mind work? What sort of things go on in their head? What are they going to do next? Can you tell?!

There is a strange poetry in the thinking of the mad. Their thought, like poetry, evokes mystery, poses riddles for the intellect to solve and, as with Magritte's paintings,[1] introduces us to things alien. So it's not surprising that most individuals, even members of the same family, find sufferers of paranoid forms of disorder to be a complete mystery – and this (perfectly understandable) lack of empathy is a real and serious barrier to all efforts to help.

In this chapter I'm going to present an example of psychotic paranoia as it develops over a period, so that you can 'travel' with the sufferer – as if observing the minutiae of their psychological processes in 'real time'. The story is actually an amalgam, a kind of collage of a family of paranoid illnesses in people I know well, all blended together into one case so as to illustrate the kinds of things that can go psychologically and socially wrong for sufferers of this problem.

Some of this information has been gathered by me through going on long walks with recovering patients and asking them about how they used to think. Other information is culled from introspection, from the empirical and psycho-dynamic literature of recent years and from my own experimental work. Some information has come from in-depth discussions during a period of over seven years with a total of 33 patients recovering from psychoses (usually schizophrenia), characterized very strongly by delusions of a persecutory nature. The actual example I'm presenting rests on about seven cases which have family resemblances beween them, with information and psychological ideas from the rest being used as a 'cement' of a kind so as to give the story continuity, sense and fluidity.

I want the reader to imagine themselves in the shoes of the sufferer and to go on this journey looking as if through their eyes at the world as events unfold. So I will use the word 'you' to describe our hypothetical character, a kind of anti-hero, and trace his steps (our character is a man) from the early days of the illness through to the final culmination. We are going to see here that the workings of the paranoid mind, although they can produce really bizarre behaviour, are not essentially that mysterious – to the extent that some people might consider themselves lucky that this scenario has never actually happened to them. I am not, however, going to make this story into a Hollywood-style action movie script. A few illnesses are like that – but many are not. In addition, the story will not be too harrowing as I have no intention of deeply distressing the reader. This is a fairly typical kind of 'psychotic scenario' which I hope will nonetheless be illuminating. It is the kind of case psychiatrists deal with many many times. So here it is: a journey into the strange but comprehensible 'world of paranoia'.

The time is the late 1970s; the place, west London. It's April and the weather is at last beginning to pick up slightly after a pretty miserable, cold, rainy autumn and winter. You are a young Indian boy, 20 years old, and you've been living in England since you were ten. But although your parents are now pretty Anglicized, you've never really quite adjusted; although the language is no problem. You're average looking, perhaps you even look a bit young for your years, you're on the small side, thick-set; but one thing going for you is that you do have a good imagination – to the extent that maybe you feel even a little 'held back'. You also have your own fair share of problems and frustrations; your real ability is not appreciated, you don't get on with anyone that well and, somehow, much to your own disgust, you keep saying or doing 'the wrong thing'. When you look back, it's true that there's been a lot of embarrassing incidents in your life – particularly due to the way you alternate between sentimental oversensitivity and brutal *in*sensitivity (from a butterfly to a bulldozer). You remember all these incidents acutely but you try to deal with the problems by dismissing them (again with brutal indifference) as trivial and of no consequence.

You have a relationship going at the moment; but, like all the rest you've had, it's not working out. You're unemployed, as she is, and you can't afford to take her out to any really nice places or ever go on any kind of spending spree. At the moment she doesn't seem that keen anyway. Sometimes you despair that you'll ever marry (even if it's arranged). You're scared to imagine being single at 60.

You often surprise your girlfriend with the things you say, which seem totally out of context and out of the blue. She accuses you of not being 'aware' and of seeming to be not 'with it'; but you don't know clearly what 'it' is, although you sense the truth in what she says. Somehow you also sense that you don't 'tick over' in quite the same way as other people, but you try not to let this upset you. You feel 'different' but you try as best you can to make a virtue out of this (perhaps you're truly unique); alas, at the moment you're not being very successful at it.

Deep down, like everyone else, you need to be acknowledged for what you are and you feel that people ought somehow to see what you have to offer – yet things just don't work out. You're also not that good at getting your message across. You have a lot going on in your head but nothing that you've ever really been able to get going in reality. You know that you're a 'special person': why doesn't anyone else realize this?

Your parents, especially your mother, make a fuss of you. They're loving really, but they also moan a lot, especially your father – criticizing you, complaining, picking you up on all kinds of things. Why won't they just let you *be*?! Why won't they ever trust your judgement, trust you to have your own mind and work things out for *yourself*? They interfere, you think to yourself, won't give you *space*, seem to think your own ideas and assessments compared to theirs are rubbish; as if you were a little boy who needs always to be looked after because he's such a worry and, basically, because he's a threat to himself. It's unfair, but then again there's a grain of truth in that. But somehow your own opinion compared to theirs is nothing. This really makes you *scream* inside at times. It stops you from ever getting started in life. But somehow you're going to break out of all this, get control of your life, get your own mind, get into the world and *be* something – someone. Unfortunately, you have no idea of just how you're ever going to do this. (Another inner scream.)

You have an older sister, very beautiful, who your parents often describe as a 'very sensible, level-headed girl'. At the moment she's away at teacher training college. Your parents' attitude to her is quite different – 'So sensible'. No, for them, her judgement is OK; it's just not fair. Sometimes you feel as if you were born into the wrong family. Somehow things just roll on getting worse and worse.

Thoughts about your father drift into your mind. Your father just won't stop talking; he goes on and on. Your own 'deliveries' are forever being interrupted in a dismissive way, as if it doesn't matter what *you* say. Again the inner scream. He revs you up. Two hours continuously with him and you feel a nervous wreck, as if you need a tranquillizer. Your mother is warm, well meaning, a good soul; but a bit 'engulfing'. She just can't get it through her head that you're not still five years old and not part of her any more. Still, you try not to think about these things. Indeed it makes you feel better not to think too much about your parents: they just won't let you have control and grow up, despite saying that they want this more than anything.

Your O-level results were really not bad at all, but you get yet another letter of rejection following a job interview. This is the one you had last week at the bank. To cap it all, a pair of skinheads mutter 'Paki bastard' as they amble past you in the street. It's a bad scene: skinheads call 'Paki bastards' at everyone with brown skin, you think. You're angry but there's nothing you can do about it without getting your head kicked in. Fascists can dish it out but they can't take it.

You wander on to the shop to get some milk and some cigarettes. You're smoking too much these days. Another boring wasted day. If only you could find just one thing to concentrate on, it would give life some meaning.

You get a week's filing work from an agency on Oxford Street; a girl called Tina rings to tell you. That's something. 'Better than a slap in the face' you think. The job is near Piccadilly. At work, midweek, it strangely occurs to you (the idea, for some reason, having a bit of force), that the world's going to end in two years' time. How strange that this idea should strike you. It *doesn't* occur to you, however, that your *own* world looks as if it's not going to last more than two years. You think it's the world as a whole. Some people at work agree with you; but some don't. This idea quite grips you for a day but then fades late in the evening as you realize it's just a bit absurd. For a day you had quite a buzz in the head which was uncannily pleasant. It makes a change – for a day you felt quite important, 'a man with a message'.

The next day you are unexpectedly shifted to a larger office, more people, more anonymous – a kind of 'filing pool'. You've been 'got rid of' you think.

You earn a standard £45 from the filing work but you decide not to declare it to the dole. It's too much hassle: interviews, forms, letters. Anyway it's only one week. Who cares? *That* system certainly doesn't care. With the money you take your girlfriend out to the Golden Gloves pub in Fulham. It seems one way to save a flagging relationship – and, anyway, you might have a laugh if you get a bit tipsy. But, again, it doesn't work out as you intended. Your girl-friend gets a little too drunk on all the spirits, makes eyes at another man and in her inebriated state belittles you in public, saying how 'silly' you talk – always going on about 'way out' things. You have a furious row in the street.

Then, when you get back home, your father is also infuri-ated at you for spending *all* your 'pocket money' on this girl and on expensive drinks when he and your mother, as he puts it 'have to work so hard to make ends meet — with no help from you'. He threatens to kick you out of the house if you ever do it again. You shout at him that it's not 'pocket money', you *earned* it! He behaves as if he never heard the remark. You stifle the urge to punch him and instead storm off into the night to ring your girlfriend from a payphone. You *must* get out of the house. But the phone just rings and rings. You slouch back home, fuming, and after making as much noise on the stairs as possible, to no apparent effect, you crawl ignominiously into bed, feeling very sick. Your father refuses to speak to you for a day.

The next time you go to sign on you are told by a slightly worried-looking counter clerk that you must wait to see the supervisor. It transpires that someone has 'shopped' you for working and signing on at the same time. The supervisor, a young white man with a poker face, gives you a good grilling but lets you off with a stiff warning ('Do this one more time and we'll have you in court!'). You spend the next few hours, which then run into days, in anguished turmoil about the interview; and wondering who had spilled the beans on you and why? It could have been almost anyone. This really sets your imagination off. You don't dare tell your parents about the whole affair, things being bad at home these days; and it looks as if your girlfriend has faded herself out of your life because when you ring, her mother says she won't talk to you.

These are bad days — and you have no real, close, friends to turn to for help or even for a talk. You didn't really mean any harm. It's all unfair. It doesn't occur to you that one way or another you do have a tendency to 'put people off'. Now you're alone — and, really, you've had a lot to do with that yourself; a bit of thought for others here and there and things might have been a lot different. But such ideas don't reach your consciousness. For some strange reason you know only your own world. You've never been able quite to 'reach' people in the first place; and yet at other times you've got in too close. It's weird. Somehow, when it comes to relationships, things have never quite 'clicked'. People, and relationships with them, don't come easily to you; you keep 'missing the bullseye' all the time. Never quite 'get it right'. But this is your life; you don't know how to do it all any differently. Deep down you feel alienated, an outsider, but you fight to keep steady and to get by. But while other people seem just to live quite easily, for you it's strangely difficult. As if you really have to 'work it out' all the time. You can't just 'live'.

You decide to do a lot of walking. It keeps you out of the house and away from your parents, and you don't want to be with people anyway. You feel pretty bad and in a strange sense 'fragile'. Trivial things are starting to seem 'significant'. The weather's pretty good now and you haven't got much money; so it seems a good idea to be out of doors. But, unfortunately, it's not. Although you think it's just something to do, little can you know that on your various travels you're going to walk yourself, one way or another, right into hell itself.

———————

It's Tuesday and you're having a stroll, after signing on. The people at Social Security were far from friendly; there was a generally and conspicuously cold atmosphere at the counter when you hurriedly penned your signature to the declaration of unemployment slip. The paper had then been brusquely pulled away from you and 'Next!' uttered brashly by the very English-looking female counter clerk. You shudder slightly as you think about the transaction. It makes you feel 'known about', as if eyes are on you. But if they are, you know that you've got nowhere to run. That inner scream again. No money until Thursday – and your father will want all of that 'to make amends'. You have 70p in your pocket, enough perhaps for a couple of cups of tea at cafes on your way. But that's all.

You meander along a road not previously known to you; 'might as well explore' you think. Three men are on the doorstep of what looks like a small office, that perhaps was once a shop but which now has a clouded glass window. As you approach, one man says to the others on the step above him, 'Yes, we'll *get him*' emphasizing the words 'get' *and* 'him'. He then happens to turn to his left and looks at you as you approach. You walk past, but all three men fall silent as you go by. You feel as if they're watching you. You cross the road (the office is on a corner) and two girls pass you when you're on the opposite side. One says to the other, looking in the direction of the office, 'Look at them Nazis'. Then it hits you. It was the offices of the *National Front*! A brick hits the bottom of your stomach.

You try to recall the slightly unsettling scenario which presented itself to you as you walked up to and then past their headquarters. Yes! He'd looked at you and then said, 'Yes, we'll *get* him!' In fact, you've *reversed* the sequence of events in memory: he'd looked at you *after* saying the words, but you have no insight into this. Also you misremember his inflexions of tone, you misrecall him emphasizing 'get', not both 'get' and 'him'. After all, it's a Fascist organization and you're 'black', a misfit and a sinner. They *would* want to 'get' you! In truth, the reality is utterly mundane; but for some reason mundane things don't interest you these days. You need something 'spectacular'.

The three men were, in fact, talking about needing an

electrician for a lighting problem in the building; but you were too lost in your own thoughts at the time to hear their earlier chatter. One had mentioned someone who was good and had a really reliable reputation and the man on the pavement had said, 'Yes, we'll *get him*'. He had not shouted the words or said them in a sinister way at all, and his look at you was merely an idle glance. But no, now the reality is lost. A reversal in memory, a slight misrecall of intonation, a guilty conscience, a feeling of being a misfit and a 'reject', boredom, stress at home, and a vulnerability to thinking what you want to think – and what was simply an everyday electrical problem has become a nasty little plot by a group of 'Fascist bastards'. Yes, they *would* pick on you, a 'foreigner', a 'drain on the state', with no big money to get a 'posh lawyer' and so on. A *pattern* starts to form in your mind.

You've always had a good imagination, maybe even too good for some people. Your mother used to wonder when you were young at your 'fantastic' drawings, your bizarre fantasies, your over-sensitivity and morbid preoccupations. You don't realize however that your imagination, which could have been your greatest gift, is now to become your deadliest enemy. Your great sensitivity, which you might have used to great effect, perhaps in the arts in some way, is also going to turn against you – as if in revenge for its neglect. What is a talent in one context can become a vulnerability in another. Now you're going to learn that; within a couple of weeks, this truth is really going to come back to you.

———————

You go home that evening with your head humming. You feel vulnerable, frightened; what you don't notice is that you're also quite excited. From a meandering 'worthless' existence, where you can't even be respected or have any impact in your own home, you are now maybe on the fringes of 'a happening'. Things are starting to move somehow, wheels starting to turn, people are, at least and at last 'taking notice', and *you* are the focus. You are in the middle of it! Unfortunately, you don't recognize the 'psychic pull' exerted by this potential escalation of the significance of your identity. You just go with the flow of your thoughts. All you really notice is that you're very apprehensive. Things *could* now be happening which are *beyond your control*. You don't notice that your *own* mind is, very slowly, starting by itself to get out of control. No, it's 'the world' that's going out of your control.

All manner of patterns start to form in your mind. Is your (now) ex-girlfriend somehow 'in on things'? Did *she* shop you to Social Security? Is *she* a Fascist? Can you *really* trust your father? Will he turn your mother against you? How did the National Front people know who you were? Who has been talking? *What* have they said?! You've suddenly got a *lot* to think about! The possibilities are endless – and there are so many unknowns! You 'realize' that you'll somehow have to work things out, work out what's going on: watch people closely, take notice of things you never bothered to look at before. Indeed you wonder whether you *dare* miss *anything*! How *many* people are against you? Who are they? There's plenty of people in your past who you've rubbed up the wrong way'. Will everything now come back at you? What will happen if all these different, and now scattered, people get to know each other? What will happen *then*?!

But no. Although your thoughts have started to race, you make an effort and subdue yourself. This is all quite ridiculous. It was just a remark. They might not have been talking about you at all. This is all just *silly*. Why do you get all these incredible ideas in your head? You don't know that there's a hint of 'creative mania' in your makeup. You calm down, settle down, dismiss it all; eventually sleep overcomes you.

The following day you set out on another walk, eager yet again to get out of the house. You start early. Your mother is surprised that you're up so early – indeed you look just a little animated, a bit 'high' perhaps, but you don't notice it in yourself. Your head is still 'humming' a little; as you think about your thoughts last night an uneasy malaise hits you. As you walk past the supermarket in the high street an elderly woman (who looks to you like a 'real far right Tory') gives you a long stare, then a teenage boy and girl seem to be looking at you and smirking as you go by. You only see them out of the corner of your eye, and, in fact, they're not looking at *you* at all; it's a 'location of gaze' error, but you don't realize this. You cryptically *expect* to be looked at. Events, a bit at a time, are starting to make you feel 'significant' in some way. Something makes you want to chase up the thoughts that occur to you as your new state of mind develops. Is anything happening *really*? You keep on walking, but now you're basically fishing for evidence.

In fact, you've done the worst thing that anyone could do in your slightly vulnerable condition – walk up the high street with dozens of people going past you, involved in their own conversations. Deep down, you really got out of the house for peace, and to calm your own arousal level, but now as you walk along you pick up *fragments* of other people's conversations and, not surprisingly, some of the words and phrases seem at least 'relevant' to you. This is tricky. Indeed on a couple of occasions that morning you hear the phrase 'It's him'. One couple say, 'He's a wally'; another person says, 'Everybody knows' and so it goes on. You went out for a quiet walk, but it's fast turning into a gauntlet of knives.

Again you try to steady yourself and go into a cafe for a cup of tea and yet another cigarette[2] to calm down. But the cup shakes as you lift it to your lips; you're more nervous than you like to admit. You gulp the hot liquid down and, paradoxically, the lift from the caffeine seems to calm you. After a long think you decide to go home by a quiet back-street route. But you're shaking a little yourself.

The following day your expected giro doesn't come. At first you panic. Do you now have no 'social security'? The very words seem to have a portentous meaning you hadn't noticed before – they're not just 'bland words'; they *mean* something. Then you realize that your earnings in the filing job have cancelled out this week's giro. You probably won't get any money until next time. Blast! But your father wants to know where the giro is. Why hasn't it come? He's forgotten you worked for a week and that's why. You realize that this could get tricky and so you tell him the truth: the whole story – about being 'done' by the Social Security and all that. However, he blows up in your face and goes into a terrifying temper tantrum. He's so disappointed with you. You can't be trusted. He calls you a dole fraud, says (wrongly), 'and now you're in trouble with the law!' and generally starts to talk and argue himself into overdrive (a little as you tend to do at times).

In fact, the whole episode could have been easily avoided; after all, he doesn't know you didn't declare your earnings. You could simply have said 'There's no giro because I worked for a week'. But in the excitement and haste neither of you is thinking very clearly. Your father continues to accelerate his rage, shouting about how he's 'always been decent and respectable' and 'never had anything like this happen to him'. At last your sobbing mother calms him down slightly, with gentle words and some looks from her tearful eyes. She has her own ways of dealing with him and shutting him up, that you just don't have. The whole scene is too much and you rush out of the house, just as your father is shouting after you, 'I haven't finished with you yet!' and your despairing mother is putting out an arm to restrain him.

Your nerves are completely 'shot to pieces' by now. There's so much *emotion* and general *racket* in that house. No *peace*. What on earth do you do now? There is *nowhere* to go.

You try going round to your ex-girlfriend's house but as you approach it you see her at an upstairs window, looking down at you with what looks like a sneer on her face. In fact, it's an illusion produced by the poor quality glass and the angle of the light. In the way that your father tends to do, you start to over-react – you begin to go into overdrive too. What is really a molehill is starting to be transformed into a mountain. Some people might think you're 'escaping from reality', but the truth is you were never *quite* part of it anyway.

You have said nothing about the National Front incident to either of your folks in case they 'don't understand' or in case they over-react once more. (Secretly, you fear that they'll say 'you were hearing things', thus rubbishing your judgement yet again.) But you notice that somehow your life is changing, things are happening – you have a strange 'feeling of meaning'. Nothing is trivial any more.

As you walk the London City streets you are starting to feel a genuinely lost soul. You decide not to go home and, instead, manage to find a fairly run-down boarding house, off the Earls Court Road, that will take you despite you being 'DHSS'. After making some promises to the landlord, you climb the long staircase and huddle into your small room, with thoughts bouncing around your mind like balls in a game of squash. The place is a dump but, because of that, you feel it's doubtful that you will ever feel compelled to leave *here*.

Your thoughts are jarring about. You don't realize that your father's lightningly sudden temper tantrum has shaken your already fragile nerves particularly dangerously, and primed you to fear a *sudden* and *unexpected* shock that might come at any moment. When you eventually venture out to a hamburger joint (with a fiver that your mother gave you yesterday evening) you now inwardly expect *anything* to happen. And, uncannily, it does. Two tough-looking young men walk past you and, after a glance your way, one says laughingly to the other, 'Yes, that's him. He's been fiddling the dole for years!'. Now the 'Fascist bastards' are *lying* about you too!

It doesn't occur to you that people often happen just to *look* at people approaching them in the street while simultaneously talking to their companion about something else. No, for you, if they look your way and say something, the two events must be connected; it must be about *you*.

You've always liked 'connecting' things, but now that too will be your enemy. You also don't notice how significant all these events make you feel: the old 'days of anonymity' are ending, *now* you're a person of consequence. But such thoughts don't get a look-in. Indeed, your stream of impressions and fears over the next few days start to rage so quickly that pretty well nothing can stop it. Things are happening too fast for insight. These are 'the days of mere survival'. Luxuries like honest, close, analytical self-scrutiny are long gone – if they ever existed. Now there's *no time*. (You don't talk to a butterfly about logic circuits.)

You also don't notice the way in which your fears of persecution are making you bend and twist some of the things you hear into what you *expect* to hear or *fear* might be being said. You're actually having incipient hallucinations. A couple at a nearby cafe table say, 'He must 'ave sense' (about somebody else) but you hear it as, 'He loves fast sex' (and you take it to be you). A man talking to his wife at another table says, 'It should be thirty-five days' (about his total annual holiday entitlement) but you hear it as 'He should be certified insane' and you assume they're talking, yet again, about you. You get up with a snarl, give him 'the evil eye' and storm out of the cafe – all eyes following you.

You don't realize that delusions can turn on a sound ('phoneme'), even be built on these phonemes. A world on a sound. And so it goes on. As you stride in anger down the road a man says to his mate, both standing outside a building site, 'I'd love a McDonalds' but you hear it as, 'I'd love to knock 'im down'. Your interpretations are starting to be dominated by erotic and aggressive drives. You always tended to be this way (which didn't help in relationships with women); but now the volume control of your emotions is being turned up and subtlety, differentiation and fine tuning is being lost.

However, your experience is what it is – and somehow you have to make sense out of it. You also have to defend yourself. In a moment of panic you scribble a letter to your MP, to the effect that you suspect that the National Front are persecuting you because you are Indian and that they have a city-wide network of people out to harass you. You fear for your safety. You have 'lots' of evidence. 'Everyone' knows and 'everyone' is against you. Your MP doesn't reply – and every day that passes with no reply makes you feel worse. But perhaps the MP is 'in' with the National Front! Yes, that would explain it. But that idea makes you feel worse still. Perhaps you should write to the Prime Minister about this? But no, you can't quite summon up the nerve.

Instead, after a few drinks you walk into a police station in Hammersmith at midnight and gabble out your story to a bunch of initially saucer-eyed but then increasingly subdued policemen. They offer, with concern, to have you spoken to that night but after noticing a 'knowing look' pass between two of them, you 'sense a plot' and carefully recant your 'silly' tale, blaming it all on drink and with measured steps, flee out of the police station up Shepherds Bush Road to Brook Green and into the darkness. Your mind is getting hot and steamy. It's a humid night too.

Now it seems that nowhere is safe. You walk aimlessly about on the grass at the green but not only are you afraid, you're getting increasingly angry. If only you could punch like a boxer, George Foreman or this young Tyson guy, then you'd show people 'a thing or two'. God, every skinhead you saw you'd 'batter'. But your own anger only provokes more fears of retribution. You have to be *very* careful now, miss nothing. The way your expectations 'suck' evidence to them like a super-powerful vacuum cleaner is an illness – but this doesn't hit you. You can only know what you experience.

A car goes past with DYE as the letters on its number plate. You take this (of course) to be a National Front insult and threat. You bet that the car was sent past deliberately so that you'd notice this. You're not even immune here, in the relative quiet and darkness of Brook Green. Where *can* you be safe?! The honk of every car horn is now directed at you. Every distant laugh from people on the main road is laughter at you. Perhaps the police have gossiped about you. There is no mercy. No-one cares. This is a world with no soul and *everyone* is against you. You always preferred to rely on yourself. You never liked being dependent – indeed you even feared it. Now you really have only got *yourself*.

But another thing that has happened at this time is that you have got an extraordinary amount of *energy*, although you do not notice this. You resolve to go to the Houses of Parliament that night, to 'see someone about all this' in the morning. It doesn't matter what time you get there; you resolve to wait outside until it opens tomorrow. *Someone* is bound to listen to you whether the MPs are there or not. After all, this is a democracy, not a Fascist regime, it's a *free country*! And something is now *definitely* going on. Yes, everything *fits* – it **must** be true!

It's too late for the tube, and you don't know which night bus to take, so you decide to walk. Being near to people in a bus is dangerous anyway. The people in the bus might 'make comments', look at you in a funny way or even attack you. The bus driver might not even stop if he notices it's *you* trying to get on. He might be National Front himself.

With seemingly inexhaustible reserves you trek east along the Hammersmith Road, all the way along Kensington High Street, past all the brightly lit shops with the west London traffic surging and lunging by you at high speed. You pause only at Knightsbridge. You notice the words are 'Knights bridge'. Can this have any 'meaning'? Is this a 'bridge' to a new life for the 'knight'?

Physically, the walk was not difficult but psychologically it was torment and has made you feel a lot worse. The *eyes* of everyone you went past seemed to drill into your mind like lasers. You don't realize that your expression now is odd and it *makes* people look at you. The sound of every car, bus and lorry was so loud, it was all so 'overloading'. The noisy engine of every vehicle that went past seemed to rev up your brain. The colours of the front and rear lights of the cars seem also to 'mean' something. Does the endless sequence of *red* rear lights symbolize blood? Is death ahead? Is it a sign?

It could be, or it could be a *test*. You fight against this deterrent.

You *have* to get to the Houses of Parliament. Somehow the idea obsesses and possesses you. At least, you thought you had to get there until you overhear a well-dressed middle-aged man say, to his wife (?) at Knightsbridge, 'There's no point in going *there*'. Since you're now grandiosely thinking that everyone's conversation is always about you and nothing else (as if they had nothing better to do), this can only mean that they've noticed you; they *know* what you're doing and discussing its futility. Your heart sinks. But how would they know what you're trying to do? This is absolutely incredible! How did they *know*? Are there 'electrodes' in your head? Have they been surreptitiously implanted while you were asleep – so your thoughts could be 'picked up'?! God Almighty! You suddenly clasp your hands to your head and *scream*.

Now you know how Munch felt. The National Front's ecstasy of power is your agony of helplessness. Pedestrians dotted around the road junctions at Knightsbridge all stare at you (the now 'Fallen Knight'). But then they hurry on their way, walking a little faster than before, the couples making comments to each other and occasionally glancing back at you nervously as they go.

Anything that in any way 'fits' with your ongoing ideas goes in, accompanied by an uncanny elevation of your feelings of certainty. Like a poet, you are secretly wallowing in the gratification of imprecise thought.[1] What you don't realize is that the balance of the activation or activity levels of the two hemispheres of your brain, up there in your head, is actually upset – so that you hungrily *persevere* with your beliefs and love to draw evidence and ideas to them that *confirms* them. But refutatory or discrepant data which would

give balance to these ideas is now very much ignored.³
You're just not processing it much; if indeed at all.

In fact, it would cause you a kind of 'psychic pain' or
inner sense of '*thought* tension' that you strangely can't bear
– despite the emotional agony you're going through. It is
certain that you can't give up your ideas *now*, that would be
to prefer ambiguity to certainty. And look how much
'evidence' you've got – and how much *time* you've put into
it all. No, no, you must *go on*, persevere even further: you
have to find out 'where all this leads'. (Even if it's to Death's
door itself). And in a bizarre way your brain is even *helping*
you to do this. After all, that's what you want, isn't it? Little
do you know that indeed it *does* lead to a Keatsian struggle at
the 'Gates of Death'. You're on a negative path, chasing it to
its terminus: and of course, the terminus is bound to be
death and destruction – unless somehow you can 'get a hold'
or, even better, get help. But no, all of these things you don't
realize. And anyway, you *like* to depend only on yourself,
remember. It doesn't occur to you to ask for help.

By a sinister but gradual process of cobweb-thin inferences, built on a spider's web of data, it doesn't hit you that
you've come from being an anonymous outsider in life to be
the living centre of a monstrous persecutory plot. Surely this
plot can only result in either your destruction, or the
destruction of your tormentors. But, you think, who *are*
your tormentors? Everybody? Does everybody *really* know
'all about you'? You're not absolutely sure – not sure enough
to act on it. Or are you? You're not even sure of this! You
need a sign; something that will 'clinch it'. But what kind of
sign? Now that it's time to act seriously, to *do* something, are
you really sure? Certainty, uncertainty, a mind within a
mind. My God! *Is* it all really happening? Yes, yes, it is,
you've thought about it all a lot, it must be. . . Yes. . . this is

it. (Unbeknown to you, the very act of thinking about it all so much in itself makes it seem more real and true.)

You walk all night and into the morning, seemingly aimlessly, but basically around the streets of Knightsbridge and South Kensington. You're looking for that 'final sign'. Eventually, before you really know where you are, you've passed Victoria and you're some way down Vauxhall Bridge Road, on the way to the River Thames. Your mind is a tormented mass of colliding images and thoughts, glowing, fading, bouncing around. 'This *is* Hell' a sinister voice in your head tells you. (You think the voice was 'sent in' via the electrodes.)

When you see a road sign with 'Vauxhall Bridge' it is 'clear' to you, as nothing in your life has ever been so clear before, what you have to do. A man says to his friend as they walk by (in fact about a show last night), 'It couldn't have gone on much longer'. Again it fits. Yes, indeed, this really is *it*. (Maybe it would have been even clearer still what you had to do if the sign had said 'Waterloo Bridge'. The night, after all, has fast shaped up to being your 'Waterloo' – the 'night of your fall'.) But the river is your only haven. Your only peace now lies surely in death.

The strident walk has changed to a shuffle. Again, you stall and meander. Daylight comes. You don't *really* want to die. But what can you do? Deep at the back of your mind you wish that someone would throw you a straw to clutch at. On the left-hand side of the Vauxhall Bridge Road, going south, you see a sign for a hospital. Ah! Perhaps the hospital can remove the electrodes! Yes! this *is* a straw but it might help. The idea that you might be mentally ill does not occur to you. The hospital is not a refuge for that reason. You pick up your stride and, with a trace of hope and optimism, you find the hospital, which is just open.

You don't know it, but this is a psychiatric hospital. You recount your tale; and eventually Nurse *Knight* and Dr *Webster*[4] recommend you be admitted immediately. They can't understand why you scream and struggle so much on being injected with anti-psychotic drugs. Your eyes are almost out on stalks; sweat pours down your forehead. But although you struggle (and cry) you don't realize how lucky you've been. Had you walked down any of the parallel roads to the river there would have been no hospital to save you. The Thames is cold and the waters run fast. People don't last long once they're in them. A different turning and you might now be dead.

Madness was a new way of thinking for you, but in fact it's a very dangerous route to take. Within a few weeks, when you're a lot better, you'll hear the drug-induced silence of your mind and be grateful. Because you know what Laing could never quite get through his head: that *madness can kill*.

4

TOWARDS PREVENTION: CAN WE AVOID DELUDED THINKING?

Prevention of mental illness is the critical aspiration, the 'higher good' of both psychologists and community mental health workers of all kinds.[1] It's usually considered under three headings: primary, secondary and tertiary prevention.

Primary prevention is the forestalling of the disorder so that it hopefully never occurs in the first place. This reduces the number of new cases, or 'incidence' of the illness. *Secondary prevention* is basically the 'nipping-in-the-bud' of a problem before it becomes serious. *Tertiary prevention* is the tackling of an established disorder, with the aim of preventing it from developing into actual disability and thence handicap.[2] Needless to say, these three categories do tend, in practice, to overlap[3] so in this chapter I will focus on primary and secondary prevention and then, in Chapter 5, which looks in part at recent therapies for paranoia, I will turn to modes of secondary and tertiary prevention. Family problems are relevant at all levels of prevention so are discussed both here and in Chapter 6. Problems in styles of thinking (so-called 'cognitive biases') are similarly relevant at all levels and are presented here and in Chapter 5.

Primary prevention

The task of preventing paranoia altogether (or indeed any other mental disorder) is not really comparable to the task, for example, of preventing jaundice, TB or even AIDs.[4] Like most mental disorders, paranoia is not usually due to a singular infectious agent or deficiency: it is the final common path of innumerable factors, variables that differ in their weighting in almost every individual – and variables that operate differently over the life course of the person. There is no possibility then of a 'magic bullet' solution.

Every human being has a genetic, organic, motivational, rational, social and spiritual aspect.[5] Factors at all these levels, not to mention the political and economic context in which we all live, are involved in producing serious paranoid disorder over time. In order to prevent its occurrence completely we literally would have to change the world radically in every way imaginable. This is out of the question.

This does not mean, however, that we're totally impotent in the face of the dilemma. This is far from the case, and in this chapter I will show why. I'm going to use a 'funnel approach' and work, so to speak, from the top downwards, in terms of scale, to try to identify the kinds of influences that, were they reversed, would likely undermine the malignancy of the problem in its many forms. I will begin with the broadest issues and work towards very specific problems in due course.

Political, social and economic context

If we take the most serious condition in which paranoia manifests itself – schizophrenia – as a guide, there is no doubt that Western ways of life can worsen the deterioration in mental health of vulnerable people. In India, for example, possibly because of the more peaceful atmospheres at home, and maybe also because of stronger family and community ties (and less stigma attached to mental illness), sufferers are less likely to relapse once they leave hospital and go back to their families. This is despite what are (usually) fewer amenities and greater poverty.[6]

With the likelihood that unemployment in the West will remain permanently high, the colossal social and psychological costs of this will also have to be maintained. Feelings of uselessness, low self-worth, depression, alienation, degradation and meaninglessness to life, will be the price millions of people will have to pay for a low inflation economy. In these circumstances, a whole host of psychological and psychosomatic disorders, paranoia included, are likely to be with us for a very long time.

It is also self-evident that 'me-first' political philosophies, with their emphasis on drive and competitiveness, are hardly likely to encourage the flowering of altruistic and cooperative qualities in ourselves and our fellow human beings. In an alienated culture of 'haves' and 'have-nots' paranoia is bound to flourish.

The problem of worker–management ('us-and-them') paranoia has bedevilled British companies for the whole of the twentieth century. This can hardly best be understood by studying people's biochemistry or brain structure; it is a problem deeply rooted in the British class system and traditions.

Worker–management alienation and division is exacerbated by many factors. These include such things as the staff/worker eating arrangements, executive share schemes and free medical attention for executives, differences in pension plan availability and in access to information about company accounts – and even by executive car parking places and such like. The elimination of these divisions and examples of favouritism (of which there are many) would at least help to break down the divides that breed and give licence for mutual suspicion.

The *secrecy* of a nation's government also inevitably breeds paranoid ideas. Without freedom of information people are naturally suspicious about 'what's on file' and ask, as indeed they do, 'Why don't they let us see our own information?'

Paranoid leaders, such as Hitler, Nixon[7] and MacCarthy, breed paranoid administrations. Blatantly hidebound governments always show a noticeable and intolerant streak of paranoia, because they know in their hearts that they deserve to be betrayed. Their knowledge of their own moral fragility makes them hypervigilant to any attempts to undermine them.

In many countries in recent times (Iraq in particular), the bulk of the population has had to tolerate such leaders who demanded complete loyalty to them – even if they were not themselves loyal to their people. Leaders abound (and have abounded) who characteristically have been unable to admit mistakes, who listened (disastrously) only to confirmatory information, who were grandiosely over-confident, with a false sense of conviction, and who hated and destroyed their 'enemies within' totally and adored their friends unthinkingly. This is a characteristic paranoid pattern. Unfortunately, although insight is impaired, intelligence and powers of logic are not necessarily clouded in such people (the great logician Gödel himself suffered from psychotic paranoia) and so such individuals can cunningly organize regimes and procedural systems around them which can bring to fruition the bizarre dreams that drive them.

It appears that a society gets the leaders it deserves. If we see the collapse of integrity in the upper echelons of our own society, we must ask ourselves whether the disappearance of integrity, care and fairness is worth the price we pay to be able to maintain our typically British docility and 'look the other way'.

Neighbourhood and subculture factors

People may group together and choose their friends on the basis of geographical proximity (e.g. through living in the same street or on the same estate) and also on the basis of shared interests, work, attitudes or sexual orientation; the latter are usually referred to as 'subcultures' or 'interest communities'. The television soap 'East Enders', for example, depicts a community based largely on the people living in the same *area*, rather than them having, say, a shared interest in gardening, fashion, poetry or whatever. People who form interest communities may live miles, even thousands of miles, apart and may generally prefer a higher level of privacy to people whose social life focuses mainly on people who simply live nearby.

As we all know, neighbourhoods can both support but (occasionally) even destroy a person. Paranoia, after all, is the other side of the coin of conformity. The benefit of conformity is freedom from paranoia. But groups of people can also *use* their own *shared* paranoia to fuel hostility against individual non-conformists, immigrants or 'deviants' – as neighbourhood gossips do and, of course, as the Nazis did against the Jews.

Human beings seem to have a natural tendency to form 'in-groups', with consequent rejection of the 'out-group'. Those who are striving hard to conform also inevitably feel hostile to others – the outsiders – who are evidently making no effort at all along the same lines. People who feel that they are outsiders in any neighbourhood usually reduce their feelings of threat by forming their own culture, and this may eventually grow into a geographical community. Many Indian and Pakistani people in Britain have done this: they have created their *own* 'in-group' to validate their shared beliefs and ways of life. This is a social protection against paranoia – although, inevitably, some residual shared group paranoia with reference to the dominant culture of the country will still exist. In London, there are also some areas so heavily populated by gay men that it is possible for a person now, at least theoretically, to *live* totally in 'the gay scene' and have little contact with the straight world – either for basic amenities or for social life.

It seems to me quite reasonable that even people recovering from clinical paranoia and delusional beliefs could *themselves* profitably form their own interest groups or cultures, where their beliefs, although taken to be strange by the main culture, would be more accepted or tolerated. This is an idea also voiced by Kenneth Heller.[8] Many societies for believers in fringe phenomena (such as UFOs, clairvoyance and the occult) have, of course, already done this. One of the great accompaniments of paranoia is *loneliness*, something which in turn can make the problem worse. Subcultures are a social answer to this vicious spiral and they can also help to 'socialize' a person's beliefs – by embedding them in shared knowledge. Criticism of the more way-out aspects of a person's beliefs is also likely to be taken better when it comes from a member of the same in-group – who is likely to be seen as basically an ally not an enemy.

Paranoia, like depression, is a condition in which a person is pervaded by *the negative*. It does not help anyone if their immediate surroundings continually trigger off pessimistic and gloomy ways of looking at the world. The general drone of a complaining or cynical parent or partner; the general drone of exposure, day after day, year after year, to a physically ugly environment; the general drone of poverty, hangovers, fights (or seeing fights), of daily, even hourly, bad news on the television, radio and in the newspapers: all of this can gradually break people down, as if they were suffering metaphorically the endless streams of mild electric shocks to the feet of a dog in a Pavlovian laboratory. Just as the dog eventually becomes ill in a variety of ways, so do people in such circumstances outlined above.

If a neighbourhood or school has a 'paranoid atmosphere' in which there is continual betrayal, criticism, slander, gossip and fast 'spreading' of information about a person, this makes paranoia very salient or significant and, therefore, more psychologically available as an attitude to hold. Most of the people I have come across with paranoid personality disorder have been reared in cultures where toughness, mistrustfulness, cynicism and disloyalty were the norm – and where people prided themselves greatly on being easily angered, not being 'a mug' and on being 'nobody's fool'. It is when a person moves out of such an anxiety-ridden culture to calmer gentler territory that the bizarre nature of their character is thrown into relief. (This, of course, in itself demonstrates that what is taken to be an abnormal or 'clinical' level of paranoia does vary from culture to culture. Levels of paranoia considered normal in the inner cities would certainly be regarded as abnormal in rural areas.)

Family problems

The ideas of R. D. Laing and his followers, on the family process origin of schizophrenia and paranoia, no longer explicitly fuel contemporary research into these conditions. But a new awareness has arisen over the last twenty years or so which does implicate the family (at least to some degree), in making its members ill. In all fairness, it's likely that the interaction of a potential sufferer and his or her family produces spiralling vicious circle problems, so that it is not possible to say that any one factor has unambiguously 'caused' the resulting problems, or illness, or that any side is necessarily 'to blame'. Nonetheless, parents who are highly over-involved with and over-protective to their offspring, while at the same time being highly critical (and perhaps also over-talkative and guilt-inducing) are *not* good for their children's mental health.[9] Too many mothers of such children worry about them excessively, tending to over-react to difficulties and smothering them with care and concern – while not allowing them to develop the coping and mastery skills that *really would* enable them to stand on their own two feet. Being continually critical and punitive, at the same time as molly-coddling children, doesn't allow for self-respect or feelings of worth or pride – they end up feeling 'no good' and helpless. This produces no benefit for anyone.

When parents are not strong enough to 'let go' and allow youngsters to have a mind of their own this also makes them feel unable to take on the world on an equal footing. Such young people are liable to feel vulnerable, incompetent, dependent and afraid. This kind of fragility can easily lead to them feeling that they are unworthy misfits in their own home – fit only to be looked after by mum and perhaps moaned at by dad. This does not induce any secure sense of self, or of self-worth, with which to face life.

Of course, the parents might say that they are only behaving this way for the child's good. The problem here is that many mothers, particularly in the first half of the twentieth century, have been socialized into a mould where they lack skills and interests outside mothering – really they can see no other way to be. Their children are the continual and only focus of their attention and concern (and overconcern). There is no way, however, that a youngster will develop his or her own life skills if they are not genuinely *respected* by their parents and are not given enough space to breathe, live and think (and, indeed, *to make mistakes*). Mothers of this ilk would be well advised to enlarge their own life's radius, take on some other interests, and thus symbolically cut their umbilical cords to their children. The latter will very likely welcome and thrive with the greater independence this gives them. If children are *trusted* to grow, rather than their every move being monitored and criticized, they very probably will. But keep them under a high-powered psychological microscope of over-attentive concern and hostility and, eventually, they're liable to curl up into a state of mental anguish.

The education of thought

It is very easy for a psychologist such as myself, working in the clinical field, to feel that somehow we should not spread our wings over into the educational field or into spiritual domains. But this timidity may well be counter-productive. We saw in the last chapter how our hypothetical paranoid character was, at the top level, the victim of real racist attitudes. He was also the partial victim of a stressful family atmosphere (but note that he had himself contributed to that stress rather more so than had his 'sensible sister'). When all is said and done, however, there's no doubt that he was also an unknowing victim of his own outrageously faulty thinking. I admit that we can hardly put blame onto his shoulders for this. When emotional intensity rises it is easy to get carried away and merely to think thoughts that somehow 'fit' with that feeling or that give licence for the feeling's expression. Nonetheless, if people had real insight into the ways that thinking can go seriously wrong then *some* measure of protection against outrageous paranoid ideas would surely be offered to them.

Therefore in this section I am going to go through (in twenty-five or so brief points) the kinds of problems that really *can* go wrong with thought itself in mental disorders of a paranoid kind. The literature on this topic is increasing all the time and the research field involved is hence a very active one. Many of the difficulties occur in 'normal' people as well but are amplified in paranoia. I will state the problems suc-cinctly in the interests of clarity and directness. Readers who would like to delve more deeply into these issues can consult the references from which these suggestions have been drawn.

1. As we have seen in previous chapters, there is a strong bias, even in quite normal people, but amplified in the paranoid and the deluded, to seek and process data and ideas that *confirm* their hypotheses at the expense of those that contradict them. This tendency to ignore contradictory evidence is particularly pernicious in paranoia where it is at its height.[10]

2. Data that does not fit with an ongoing hypothesis is also very easily avoided and forgotten. This means that the pool of remembered events that confirm a paranoid idea grows with little or no competition from material that would discredit it.[11]

3.   Events which, at the time that they occurred, seem genuinely ambiguous, can become spuriously *un*ambiguous with the passage of time, as they become embedded in the person's knowledge and belief system. This again gives them a confirmatory status that they do not deserve.[12]

4.   Paranoid individuals very often choose interpretations of events that are far more *spectacular* than the mundane reality.[13]

5.   Related to point 4, it is very dangerous to put spectacular interpretations onto events which happen to be congruent with ongoing thoughts. (For example, a girl on a train looks up just as you're thinking how pretty she is. The mundane interpretation is that she looks at you because you're looking at her: not because she has extra-sensory perception.) The overweighting of the occurrence of such 'congruent' events is called *illusory correlation*. We remember such 'meaningful' correspondences *better* than random co-occurrences – and hence we over-represent them in long-term memory and claim how many 'uncanny' coincidences have occurred. (Unfortunately, psychotherapists are also very vulnerable to this phenomenon.)[14] Thousands of events 'cross-connect' to ongoing thoughts during our lifetimes simply on a chance basis.[15] Sadly, paranoid people are such seekers after meaning that they have less tolerance of randomness than more banal thinkers.

6.   The subjective estimate of the number of times events of a certain kind have happened is inflated, the more often you think of these events.[16]

7. The longer you think about something the more real it becomes, or the more sure you become that it is true or that it really happened, even if it didn't.[17]

8. We all have a tendency to aim at internal *consistency* at the expense of truth. It is important to try and tolerate contradictions; admit you don't know, don't *force* consistency. This capacity is what Keats used to refer to as 'negative capability'.[18]

9. If information comes along which is discrepant with or contradicts our ongoing hypotheses, we have a strong tendency simply to disbelieve it.[19] It is important to beware of this.

10: Paranoid and deluded people tend to be over-confident about hypotheses that are, in fact, wrong. It is best to match confidence with the quality of the evidence.[20,21]

11. There is a tendency in normal people, which is very noticeable in the conversation of deluded patients, to 'jump to conclusions' – to take the first idea or explanation that comes to mind. This is called the 'availability bias'.[22]

12. The causes we ascribe to events are often based on stereotypes (well-worn explanations available in our culture) rather than reality.[23]

13. It is a sad fact that we don't always discriminate accurately between memories of reality and memories of fantasies and dreams.[24]

14. *Recent* experiences have a disproportionate effect on our judgement.[25]

15. It is a particularly unfortunate fact that people who 'stand out' in some way, e.g. a black person among whites, a woman among men, etc., not only attracts more attention but also receives more extreme evaluations. This can lead to such 'salient' people being stereotyped and misperceived in general.[26] Needless to say, it is easy for sensitive misfits to realize this and become genuinely paranoid for good reason. This is one of the many ways that paranoia can result from genuine unfair treatment while producing the effects of a vicious circle.

16. It is very easy to blame other people's intentions self-defensively for *bad* events in your life, but to take the credit for good events. The price of this inflation of your self-worth is a certain measure of paranoia.[27]

17. Deluded people believe their own imaginings more than normal people believe theirs. But they believe clear reality-derived evidence *less* than do normal people. This is noticeable not only in the throes of paranoid delusions but even on straightforward laboratory tasks.[28]

18. Paranoid people strangely neglect to recognize that confirmation of their ideas can be *due to* their own sometimes offensive behaviour towards others. This insight problem can produce a life dominated by vicious circles, and self-fulfilling prophesies.

19. It is not always definite that paranoid people hold their odd beliefs with utter conviction. Often the person lives in a strange double reality in which they both believe and simultaneously *don't* believe their constellation of thoughts.[29] It is important that the

sufferer face head-on this double aspect to their existence and air their reasons for their disbelief, so that their thinking can be shared and discussed. It is possible that a critical *test* of their beliefs could be devised.

20. Related to point 19, paranoia involves a curious mix of risk and caution. The (in a sense risky) belief may be held onto in a spirit of caution. So, 'when in doubt fear the worst',[30] yet in a more balanced mood the same belief might be seen as *really* highly questionable. To give it up needs the strength to face the terror of *trust*.

21. The more explicitly and specifically social dimension to paranoid thinking is usually riddled with biases. For example, sufferers tend to assume there is lightning fast and space-age efficient communication between the people who are against them. If they have a sneezing fit in the street it will be 'known' at 'headquarters' within minutes. Similarly so if they have a violent argument with their spouse. They also tend to assume 'biased penetrance' i.e. the neighbours can hear them, through walls, even if they can't hear the neighbours – through *the same* walls! Paranoia sufferers also overestimate others' degree of concern with them and interest in them, and fail to grasp fully that others really do have lives of their own – utterly independent of anything they themselves do or say. One can see here why paranoia can be both triggered by loneliness, making the person out-of-touch in the way they think socially, and simultaneously a defence against loneliness and feelings of isolation.

22. Just as the universe abhors a vacuum, the mind abhors randomness. In madness this abhorrence is multiplied a hundredfold. People in the throes of delusional crises notice everything and can ignore *nothing*. It is not the intensity of the overload that is critical, it is the *semantic implications* (all the possible connotations of the words) in the continual rain of stimuli: so that 'everything *means* something' and 'nothing is trivial'. Beware of allowing this state of mind to encroach – an independent mentality in a cut-off loner is no use if this kind of over-processing starts to occur. Be brave enough to ask for *help*.

23. Our minds are designed to infer the *causes* of events and generally we are pretty good at it. Nonetheless, this process can go wrong in paranoia. For example, some people are consistently nasty with everyone all the time so the cause of their nastiness is internal to themselves. When a paranoid person meets someone who is like this they tend, however, to think that the offensive person, say some shopkeeper or bus conductor, *is only nasty with them* and hence *they themselves* (the victim) are the cause of the person's upsetting behaviour. They then defend against this blow to self-esteem by blaming 'the world', 'everyone' etc. When dealing with difficult or insulting people, it is important to consider that the *cause* of their behaviour towards their victim could well lie in them, not in oneself. There is then no reason to defend against the blow to self-esteem with paranoid ideas: the offensive behaviour often has nothing to do with the recipient at all.

24. Paranoid people can often have a certain manic

quality to their thinking (see Chapter 1); they crave mental pleasure. This can make them simply believe the thought that gives them the biggest *thrill*, rather than the most solid and appropriate (if mundane) thought.[31]

25. A person can become habitually aggressive if they continually infer, even in genuinely ambiguous circumstances, *negative intent* in other people for bad outcomes. (For example, someone inadvertently treads on your watch when it falls off your wrist onto the pavement so you – stupidly – hit them.)[32]

26. Finally, if you're prone to paranoia you're likely to infer external causes in preference to internal ones. So if you notice people 'whispering' you're likely to think they're planning or plotting something (this is an 'external' instance). In fact, you could be going *deaf* (internal). Notice and think about internal or even spiritual factors before you jump to the conclusion that something that's troubling you is 'external' or concrete. For example, if you feel strangely passive or fragile, this could be a *mystical* experience rather than one of 'computer control of the mind'. Also, if your mind is 'full of ideas' etc., this could also be a creative-mystical experience rather than one of 'thought implantation by rays'.[33,34]

As can be seen, many of these biases overlap and dovetail together. For example, the drive to consistency tends to fuel the avid seeking of confirmatory information. In the last example given above, the person is jumping to conclusions, hastily seeking a 'thrilling' spectacular interpretation, looking for answers *outside* themselves and misreading passivity feelings as due to an external controlling agent. (This last we refer to as attributing a cause to an 'external locus of control'.)

In looking at the problem of prevention of paranoia, it's clear that we cannot focus our mental gaze just on one level as if we were focusing our eyes only at one plane or surface ahead of us. We have to 'defocus' to broad issues but also home in to scrutinize very particular problems. Paranoia is a phenomenon which threads its way through human life at every level of description — and, of course, without the processes that lead to paranoia we would have no creativity.

5

UNDERSTANDING AND TREATMENT: RECENT DEVELOPMENTS

The 'self' in psychosis

I ask you . . . what do you think of *yourself*? Although we don't often explicitly and bluntly ask ourselves this question, the hidden processes of self evaluation are ongoing in much of our daily lives. Do you *like* yourself? Are you getting closer to your image of what you'd really like to be as you get older? Or further away from it? Do you have a firm sense of who and what you are? Do you like your body? Or hate it?!

All of these questions relate to what psychologists call 'the self-concept'. This is an umbrella term for all our thoughts (and feelings) about our self; of course, these thoughts and feelings are quite varied and numerous, so the self-concept has many sides to it.[1]

Psychiatrists and counsellors have been interested in the role of the self-concept in mental disorder for many decades,[2] however, there has been a resurgence of interest in the last few years by experimental psychologists in the part it has to play in mediating psychoses, including paranoia.

What and how we think of ourselves has a major effect on

our general 'cognitive' processes and capacities for decision making. If you have ever had the misfortune to mix with people who regarded you as 'all wrong', where for them everything you did and said was somehow out of place or silly, you may remember how such an experience of 'invalidation of the self' can play havoc with your whole mind and every mental operation currently going on in it. You start to doubt yourself at every juncture, you forget things, start to forget what you were about to say, hesitate a lot, your timing goes, you lose your sense of humour, and so on. Invalidation of the self interferes with everything. Not surprisingly, then, psychologists are increasingly keen to devise measures which assess the self-concept accurately and to study how 'deep damage' to it can produce mental illness.

Every human being's interpretation of life is an interpretation of a world inclusive of themselves. The person is at the centre and is part of their own creation. When we interpret life: it is as if we photograph ourselves in the act of photographing the world. How we think and feel about ourselves therefore has a massive effect on what we make out of existence. Do we consider ourselves as a victim, a saint, a sinner, a nonentity in relation to the cosmos — or what? Delusions must therefore inevitably reflect the person's own self-perception and their unique contribution as part of a greater whole. We relate to existence also as part of it.

What is critical here seems to be the issue of how *worthy* a person feels themselves to be. The level of their self-worth or, in slightly drier language, 'self-esteem', turns out to be very difficult to measure, because the way a person *likes* to think of themselves and what, deep down, they actually *do* think of themselves can be very different.[3] It is natural for people to try and find ways of boosting their feelings of self-worth. We may compare ourselves to people worse off or inferior to ourselves, strive to win competitions, seek prizes and prestige, improve ourselves and our situation materially; but also we can *lie* to ourselves and deny or disown our negative intents, failings and weaknesses. These defensive processes seem particularly pertinent in the case of paranoia and are a useful concept for linking theories of the emotional and of the intellectual processes involved in delusional thinking.[3]

Much research suggests that anxious, insecure and self-deprecating people have a large gap between how they perceive themselves actually to be and their idea of their 'ideal self'.[4] But even this is a tricky issue as a person may be close to their ideal self in some aspects of their lives (e.g. financial status, prowess at sport), but far away from it in others (e.g. social skills, physical attractiveness).[5] The self–concept is a multi-faceted diamond. Nonetheless, although it is true that a small discrepancy is not necessarily a good measure of adjustment, speaking generally, large actual self–ideal self discrepancy is usually a source of mental pain of one kind or another. If a person tries to avoid this mental pain by creating a distorted image of themselves in their own mind this discrepancy can be much reduced. On questionnaires dealing with this, paranoid patients can even have zero or minimal actual–ideal self difference![6] This is the motivational source of paranoid grandiosity.

Another defensive technique to minimize the difference is to credit oneself for all the good things in one's life but to blame everyone else for all the bad things. Even quite normal people show this so-called 'self-serving bias' but it is greatly exaggerated in paranoid and deluded patients. Its function could well be to protect a damaged sense of self-worth.[7]

To try and prove this, researchers have devised subtle techniques to bypass defensive processes. Defences take *time* to be activated, they are not lightning fast[8] – so fairly obvious techniques, where a person has the opportunity to marshall their self-protective strategies, turn out to produce quite different results from techniques where the person doesn't realize that self-worth related issues are under scrutiny. Then what they *really* think and feel about themselves comes through.[9]

The way it works out is that, when paranoid patients are asked by quite transparent questions to find *causes* for positive and for negative events, they attribute positive events (e.g. success at work) to *internal* causes (to do with the self) but negative events to external causes and to others (e.g. the business failed due to the recession). However, when the defence-penetrating methods are used paranoids do indeed attribute the cause of negative events to *themselves* and the cause of positive events to others.[10] It seems that when very fast acting, 'implicit' processes are tapped, rather like Freud's unconscious processes,[11] the truth comes out. This, of course, is why 'Freudian slips' occur: the usual defence mechanism hasn't been executed or hasn't operated in time.

Although we're not sure of this it also seems that paranoid people, like depressed people, think the causes of events will last a long time ('stable' attribution) and that they will have wide-reaching effects on their lives ('global' attribution).[12] These are obviously pretty damaging ways of thinking if they're applied to negative outcomes.

Another difficult factor, however, is just *why* paranoid people operate this defensive process of blaming others for negative outcomes when depressed patients do not. (Depressed people are fairly even-handed about their blame for negative outcomes when the revealing technique is defence-facilitating, but blame themselves when it is defence-penetrating.)[13] It could well be that paranoids are rarely paranoid for no good reason: and, indeed, increasing

numbers of investigators are realizing that sufferers of paranoia have often been the real victims of conspiracy. What the
psychiatrist, Dr N. Cameron, used (in the 1940s) to call 'the
paranoid pseudocommunity' is often in part *real* not illusory.[14] Over the years, of course, this induces the person to
look for external causes and since finding external causes
makes a person distressed, self conscious, angry, unlikeable
etc., this can produce a perpetuating vicious circle.

The finding, however, that when defences are penetrated
the paranoid person does nonetheless tend to take personal
responsibility for difficulties and failures in their life, shows
that they do in truth also feel pretty miserable about themselves. The origin of this probably lies partly in childhood
and teenage experiences at home[15] and/or in their school
years. Over-involved parents who lay 'guilt-trips' on their
children, sensitize them to threat by excessive criticism,
show them no real love and respect *for who they are* and
schools where bullying, ridicule and shaming are rife, may all
play a part in the creation of this deep damage. It is easy to
see how basically cruel and *unfair* people can bring about this
double reality in the suspicious mind, where they are both
'to blame' and yet not to blame.

The presence of defensive processes in the creation of
paranoia was first suggested by Freud[16] who recognized that
delusions can be an attempt to repair psychic damage.
Although such 'delusionwork' may superficially have this
effect, the cost is a considerable discrepancy between how
the person sees themselves and how they are viewed by
others.[17] In the extreme, some patients convince themselves
that they are an all-powerful but persecuted Christ; yet the
reality of their situation is that they are a 'Kafkaesque' figure,
sat in seclusion in a psychiatric unit, totally dependent on all
around them for the satisfaction of their basic needs. This can

be the result of the mistrust of the judgement of unfair others, and compensatory inflation of the self, taken to its 'logical' conclusion.

The experience of having one's secrets revealed – as frequently happens – does terrible damage to a person with an already insecure sense of who and what they are, and a seriously negative view of themselves. This insult to the self, the feelings of being invaded (like a piece of cheese by mice), is probably involved in the causation of hallucinations, where a person feels that other people have penetrated their mind and are talking to them and about them right there inside their own head. People who suffer this dreadful symptom often say that they feel 'transparent' and that the boundary where their self ends and the rest of the world begins is 'blurry'. This can strangely co-exist nonetheless with great feelings of self consciousness: and we find that people who are highly self conscious do tend to be more paranoid.[18]

Research on the self, and on attributional processes in psychosis, is currently a very active area and it also holds out the promise of greater rapprochement between experimental psychology and the vast body of knowledge that began with Freud which is known as psychoanalysis.[3, 19] This can only be for the good, as psychoanalysis critically studies the *motivational* processes of people. Without knowing what it is that the person is really trying to do, both consciously and unconsciously, explicitly and implicitly, we cannot get a full picture of the suspicious mind.

Dealing with new information

Another area of current research in paranoia looks closely at how patients search for, receive and process the information in the world around them. Not surprisingly, there is a

number of biases which patients demonstrate here: many of
these are also shared by people who believe in the paranormal – a possible reason why delusional belief systems
often co-exist with beliefs in extra-sensory perception,
'thought rays' and the like.[20]

Characteristics of both paranoid patients[24] and believers in
the paranormal[24] can include: seeing 'meaningful connections'
between truly randomly paired words and events; selectively
seeking confirmatory information; failing to evaluate novel
discrediting information; jumping to hasty conclusions and
being over-confident about, in fact, very questionable ideas.
But, interestingly, it has to be said that the vast bulk of such
believers, like the paranoids, think the way they do because of
compelling *real* events which were genuinely uncanny.[21, 24] It
seems that once such systems of thought are induced by real
events, their *maintenance* and *elaboration* is produced by quite
different factors and here, sadly, cognitive biases play an
important role.[22, 24] Nonetheless, it must also be said that just
as the paranoid person's attitude may help to bring about real
events of persecution, the very open-minded, even gullible,
attitude of some people may make them more open to paranormal forces. There is quite a body of research that demonstrates that this is so.[23]

Research is, in addition, suggesting that the general high
level of agitation and stress in the course of an evolving
mental illness has a serious effect on a person's mental
capacity to think clearly, critically and realistically.[24] Mental
capacity seems to be reduced at very high levels of arousal[25]
and alertness, so that the more complex thought processes,
involved in adjusting to novel information which requires
radical changes in the way someone thinks, are simply not
possible. Hasty, confirmation-seeking, thought therefore
seems to dominate, as it is much easier and less cognitively

stressful.[26] (Among psychologists this is known as a bias to 'assimilation' over 'accommodation'.)

Thinking in this 'one-track-minded' fashion can result in great creativity, at least in the singular paranoid direction, and people with a strong tendency to confirmation-seeking thought do tend to be more creative. However, where thinking requires 'many-track-mindedness' (real divergency of thought), these paranoids are at a disadvantage and generally do worse than non-paranoid patients, neurotic people and normal people.[27] This is a serious disadvantage when several potential solutions to a problem need to be created and thought through. Indeed it has been found that suicide survivors show such rigidity of thought[28] and this may be one reason why they could think only of suicide – and little else – as a solution to their dilemmas in life.

'Cognitive-behavioural' treatment for delusions

The great strides forward that have been made in the understanding of paranoid thought, even in the last few years, strongly indicate that attempts to change such thinking and behaviour should take advantage of our knowledge of normal thought and belief processes. It is now outdated to regard paranoid beliefs as somehow radically and qualitatively different from normal beliefs, or to think that drugs and not words are 'the only answer'.

Paranoid beliefs have a 'double-reality status' to them in many ways. In one sense, other people are to blame; in another, the sufferer himself or herself is to blame. In one sense, the world is operating as it usually does; in another sense, it is all 'false', a 'put-on', in fact 'strange things are going on'. In one sense the sufferer believes in these strange convictions, yet sometimes does not — sometimes wavers and questions them. People are treating the sufferer fairly, yet unfairly. The victim longs for the certainty that a real acid *test* of their beliefs would bring; yet they also fear it, preferring to simmer in the ambiguous twilight world of their own private but unshared 'conviction'. Our real challenge is: how can we bring a person out of their twilight world into the daylight of shared reality? Could they take this if we did or would they become horrifically anxious?[29] Do they desperately *need* their beliefs?[30]

Like most normal people, paranoia sufferers rarely put their beliefs to an acid test. Also, like normal people (including scientists), they cannot be easily and straightforwardly argued out of their beliefs unless this is attempted at a very early stage of their formation.[31] Like most individuals, paranoid people will not test their ideas unless they are significantly unsure of them anyway[32] and they won't *change* them until they have an alternative belief to move to.[33] Researchers who have worked on cognitive-behavioural methods of modifying delusional beliefs also agree that a really confrontational challenge to the belief is to be avoided; as this is likely, if anything, to reinforce it rather than weaken it.[34]

Although it is generally agreed that *traditional* psychotherapeutic approaches to paranoia meet with very limited success, words can still be useful. Acknowledging with the sufferer that they must have reasons and evidence to hold to what they do, and that they are not utterly stupid and deranged, is a useful starting point. This approach does not undermine self-worth and it establishes that the helper and the sufferer have some common ground of mutual respect and knowledge on which to stand. It establishes what is known as 'joint reference'.[35] Without such joint reference no useful therapy (or indeed teaching or research!) can be done.

Looking carefully, and again with respect, at the evidence for the belief, in a graded sequence[36] from least important and plausible to most important and plausible is a useful rapport-building exercise. While this is being done alternative explanations can be suggested for the evidence raised. It is also important to agree with the sufferer what evidence *could* discredit their delusion, what would have to happen for them to admit its falsity one way or another.[37] (For example, if they think they can predict what a newsreader is going to say, it would be possible to video a news broadcast, stop it at a certain point in the delivery, and ask the person to try and do just that.)

Most sufferers are prepared to discuss, with a sympathetic and respectful listener, alternative interpretations of the evidence they have; but not all are willing, or indeed suitable, for unambiguous testing of their beliefs against reality. Some such tests can be exceedingly stressful. In other cases, a critical test that they agree would be a 'decider' is simply impossible to create (e.g. it would be difficult to test the belief 'MI5 are circulating a photograph taken of me in a compromising position'). As another example, a young man who had an actual delusion about the National Front (which formed the rough basis of Chapter 3 here) would not allow me to go round to the National Front offices to question them about any campaign they might have had to persecute him. Not only would such an intervention be dreadfully stressful for him, he would not agree that it would be a definitive test. Even the hiring of a private investigator could not have decided the issue one way or another, as this young man's particular delusion was intrinsically irrefutable – as some delusions are. In another case a young woman would not allow me to tape-record surreptitiously what some young men were saying as they walked past her flat on the way home from the pub. She believed they were mocking her every night but the actual act of collecting the evidence to study it carefully was too stressful for her.

In other instances the delusion is so clearly a motivated belief, and strangely 'needed' for the sufferer's equilibrium, that much is required to build up their feelings of self-worth, in a relationship of mutual trust and respect, and to ease guilt and shame feelings — long before delusion removal is even attempted.

Although a delusion can seem a clever way for the self to protect itself against feelings of worthlessness, most delusions do eventually become their possessor's worst enemy. They are like a bizarre mask that eats away at the face of the person who wears it. For this reason — and here the decision to test reality has to be based on expert clinical judgement — the reality-testing removal of a delusion can make a person feel *less* not more depressed[38], and give their life a new and wider radius than when it was cramped by their vice-like thoughts.

The finding of alternative interpretations for delusional thoughts, and the acid testing of delusions against reality, are genuinely valuable techniques that can at least reduce conviction and sometimes even eliminate delusions altogether.[39] They have only become possible, however, through us seeing psychotic paranoid thinking as a process of interpretation of life experiences and a way of making sense out of one's current scenario (i.e. like normal belief formation). There is now no reasonable doubt that paranoid thinking itself is faulty, but not so disastrously so that the sufferer cannot be helped, understood or empathized with at all. Cognitive distortions often occur even in normal people, not only under the influence of expectancies and 'poor memory' etc.

but under the pressure of emotional and motivational forces (sometimes people think what they *must* think for their own self preservation). The effects of agitation, anxiety, anger, guilt and dread not only shape the contents of a delusion but help to mediate the mistakes and illusions that allow it to become lodged in place and maintained. It is therefore critical that the motivational and emotional life of the paranoid person is not ignored.[40]

Reality testing comprises a number of techniques which, in fact, deserve wider use. Tests, for example using video, which can be done in the treatment unit ('unit-based tests') allow a much greater degree of control than those that have to be done in the community ('community-based tests'), e.g. questioning workmates or neighbours. For example, one man who believed he was forever being stared at in public, and being made the victim of disparaging remarks, eventually improved sufficiently with psychotherapy and counselling, and his feelings of self-worth were so improved, that community-based tests which were instigated to see if his fears were true were abandoned. In fact, I decided that if tests of this kind did eventually prove positive (and people can very easily stare and make cryptic snide remarks about a person's appearance in the street) it could have done him considerable damage.

Where delusions involve belief in paranormal powers, or where the person believes that they have capacities to influence what happens on television, unit-based tests are much easier and delusion-discrediting outcomes have been found to be therapeutic.[41] But if a person believes that sordid rumours are circulating about him in his neighbourhood, a unit-based test is not viable and the 'delusion' may really need to be researched out there in the community. (Unfortunately, because of staff and time shortages, few mental health organizations of any kind have the facilities to do this.)

The outcome of laboratory and clinic-based research in paranoia in recent years has been a growing awareness of the need to treat the patient's defences tenderly.[42] We also have an increased awareness that their deep feelings of worthlessness or low self-worth, although they often conceal them to others and even to themselves, have to be improved.[43] It is critical that therapists do not try to rip aside the patient's defences and ridicule their illusions about themselves in the interests of making them 'face up to bedrock truth'. The person's feelings of self-worth can undoubtedly be improved by a positive, patient, caring therapist who genuinely likes the person for who and what they are[44] and indeed, this may be the necessary form of therapy in some cases before cognitive and behavioural interventions (such as those discussed above) can be implemented.[40]

On 'hearing things'

Paranoid sensitivity is very often accompanied by the agonizing symptom of hallucinations. These are usually – but not always – auditory (unlike on LSD trips where they tend to be visual) and hence they involve the experience of internal voices which are taken to be real.

The symptoms of hallucinations have received considerable attention from researchers in recent years and we have good reason to believe that these are largely *internally*-generated phenomena, which are mis-attributed by the sufferer to an external source. Clearly this is also a defect in the Self, in that the person is not able to think efficiently about their own perceptions and thoughts, and about external reality.[45] We also now know that, like delusions, this group of symptoms can exist on a continuum with normal functioning[46] and that a variable degree of susceptibility to hallucinations exists in the normal population. Moreover, we know that stress, *context* and *expectations* can influence the onset of hallucinations, both what is heard and where it is heard[47] and that noisy surroundings (such as busy streets) facilitate hallucinations better than hearing clear meaningful speech. (So, as for delusions, rather impoverished external input is also important.)[48] Some recovering patients deliberately avoid situations where people are talking not *quite* out of earshot, and situations where there is moderately (but not *very*) noisy machinery, as these scenarios tend to provoke their 'voices'.[49]

It seems that hallucinations, although they involve the experience of passivity, paradoxically also involve active constructive processes on the part of the sufferer. They essentially 'make' them mentally in response either to sensory isolation or out of the roughage of 'impoverished ambiguous input' – but do not realize that they are doing this.

The case for seeing anti-psychotic medication as helpful for reducing these experiences is unclear – at least in patients suffering their first illness.[50] But other techniques (although in their infancy) do show some promise.[48] For example, one man, in the early stages of hallucinations, *masked* them totally from 7 a.m. to 11 p.m. each day by playing Radio One at sufficient loudness to make them inaudible. Although his hallucinations had previously been level in loudness, after this they became progressively fainter each day and, in a week, were gone. A similar project using radio headphones also proved effective, although only when the headphones were actually worn.[51]

The forewarning of situations which may generate hallucinations may also be helpful. There are certain situations which can 'throw up' self-referenced sounds very easily, and patients are generally eased in their anxieties by knowing about these.

Perception researchers have known for a long time that expectations can make us see and hear what is simply not there – even in isolation – but especially when *some* rough material is there for us to 'process'.[52] For example, the auditory threshold for hearing our own name is extremely low, so we can sometimes think we hear our name mentioned when in fact it has not been spoken. I remember myself once mishearing 'pieces of chewing gum' as 'Peter Chadwick' (!) Instances of this kind abound in every day life. For example, English people entering a pub full of Welsh speakers are often convinced that they are being talked about by the people in there – whom they cannot understand at all! In mental disorder, however, this creative constructive capacity seems to be massively amplified – and all manner of things can thus be 'heard' which are, in fact, quite other than what the sufferer experiences them to be. In Chapter 3 we saw our character mishearing, 'he must 'ave sense' as, 'he loves fast sex' (an actual example). The muffled voices of neighbours through thin walls provide many, even more spectacular, examples than this.[53]

Knowledge about the extent to which these symptoms are indeed *self created* is in itself of some therapeutic value,[48] so I will stress this aspect here. The fragments of sounds (phonemes) from a barely heard utterance can easily be used (imaginatively) by paranoia sufferers to build fantasy sentences. The *order* of the phonemes can even be reversed in the final product and new and additional sounds added ('phoneme reassembly') to create what the person not only thought they heard but *really does* 'hear'. So, for example, 'Look Mam, there's a McDonald's' becomes, 'Look Mam, there's that man they're going to knock down' (another actual example, slightly modified in Chapter 3). Clearly, expectations and fears are motivating this reassembly.

In other cases, *intersections* of *two* utterances (particularly if said in similar tones) can produce illusory single words or even sentences. For example, 'devious' and 'well' said simultaneously by two different people can produce the more sinister 'devil' (as if said by one person); 'Madonna' plus 'workman' can produce 'madman'; 'easy' plus 'villain' can produce 'evil' – and so on. At a sentence level, 'She's had an offer' intersecting with, 'He's tried it, no good' becomes, 'She's had it, no good'!

Word reversals can also occur so that 'his watch' becomes 'watch him'. Given these phenomena it is not surprising that paranoid people can find cacophanies of (usually) moderate intensity sound, as in streets, cafes, refectories and football crowds, very stressful – particularly when they have the sense that everything is 'meaningful' upon them. It is much better to avoid such places when this 'meaning feeling'[54] is present. However, it is nonetheless valuable for sufferers to be knowledgeable about these tricks that a mind can play on itself as this knowledge tends to be stress reducing, it helps the person deal with shock and surprise and, indeed, it helps them to *manage* their own perceptions and thoughts.

In perception, our senses search the world and we are *continually* forming hypotheses about the roughage that we gather, basically what it *means* in terms of words, objects, people etc. so that we can make sense of our surroundings.[55] We don't realize that we're doing this until the process breaks down or goes wrong – rather in the manner that we don't know how our car works until it breaks down! For example, I was talking to my wife late one night and was telling her that I had gone out far too early for a tutorial I had given earlier that evening. She asked me what I'd done to fill the time before the tutorial began and I said, 'I went to a hamburger joint'. She replied, 'Oh! I thought you were going to say "I went to Hamburger Joe's".' Obviously the hypothesis 'Joe's' had occurred almost *immediately* I had uttered the 'j'. She only realized that she had constructed this hypothesis when it was discredited by the word 'joint'. (Note also that the formation of it had made her mask out in memory the 'a' that I had said.) This shows starkly how *fast* these hypotheses form and occur, and how tricky the processes are. It is often our illusions and mistakes that therefore reveal to us, as of course in madness, the remarkable efficiency, acrobatic speed and wonder of the human mind.[56]

One of the problems intrinsic to madness is lack of insight. Another is hastiness and over-confidence in decisions.[48] It is my hope that people who read this chapter (and, indeed, this book), will start to get an inkling of what goes on beneath the surface of 'psychotic hypotheses, and eventually come to realize why psychiatrists do not tend to take them at face value. In illnesses of these kinds the path to health is through humility: but this also includes a sense of humility in the face of the intricacies of the very organ – the brain – which has mediated that experience of insanity. In a sense our consciousness sits on the top of a giant 'dream factory' – the complexity of which we have only just begun, really over the last century or so, to fathom.

The challenge of empathy

People who are highly paranoid are also highly empathic.[57] Empathy is the ability to understand and comprehend another person's experience, to place yourself as if in their shoes and look out at the world through their eyes, feeling what they feel, knowing what they know. It may be this attribute that enables paranoid people to discriminate real from sham emotion so well – as indeed they can.[58] But just as paranoia is a price people pay for the capacity to perceive relations and order, so it is the price of extreme empathy.

Great powers of empathy as, for example, possessed by the tragic Van Gogh, have to be controlled. To focus on the deceptive, and on the buried and secret negative aspects of the world (to which paranoids seem able to resonate), gives no peace or functional effectiveness in life – except perhaps in dealing with sadists, psychopaths and confidence tricksters. Empathy, like any capacity, be it conscientiousness, musical intelligence or physical power, has to be tuned and modulated for its benefits to be fully realized. The positive utilization of paranoid people's great empathic capabilities can be a route to more productive living.

Having said this, however, mental health professionals working with paranoia sufferers also need to reap the benefits of a positive orientation for themselves. For example, the high frequency with which sufferers of delusions report instances of the spontaneous paranormal[24, 41] usually meets with arrogant or cold dismissal from therapists – who may even see such claims as signs of 'illness'. But we now have experimental evidence which demonstrates that strong empathic links do indeed enhance paranormal connections.[59] The great capacity possessed by paranoid people for reading the minutiae of body language, likewise usually meets with denial from therapists. When the patient says that the therapist is 'full of anger' the latter usually throws this back in their face as a prototypical example of 'projection'. But paranoids can indeed often read moods exceedingly well[24] – maybe too well for their own good.

Examples such as these confront society with the dilemma of how to face up to the challenge of acknowledging the importance of empathy in paranoia as well as the challenge of paranoid people themselves. Transpersonal psychologists postulate the existence of a deeper substrate to mental life: a Cosmic Mind or World Soul.[60] In resonating to the deepest levels of the psyche it is feasible that the paranoid individual reflects (or indwells in) an aspect of all humanity. It is true that this is a negative aspect, but of a kind that, even when all associated illusions are stripped away, still has a trace of essential validity. In some cases, such as that of Adolf Hitler (himself a man of renowned and uncanny empathy), they can even take advantage of this 'deep access' to the half-wishes of millions to steer them into the streets and alleyways of hell.

At its deepest roots paranoia is therefore a spiritual phenomenon, as well as involving spiritual problems. Every paranoid person has been shaped into what they are by life, by the world. They reflect the world as they have known it, at the deepest of levels, *right back at itself*. And in doing this they confront that world with a facet of its own image. This is the source of the real terror that all people feel at the threat of the paranoid mind.

6

SOME FAMILY AND
RELATIONSHIP ISSUES

Biological and psychological treatment

Genetic and neurological factors (on their own) do not – as far as we know – cause schizophrenia and paranoid psychoses, which makes it unlikely that medical treatment on its own can cure them.[1] Anti-psychotic drugs themselves can also have distressing and, in some cases, even dangerous side effects,[2] in the form of permanent movement disorder,[3] for example. It is not even true that patients on drugs always do better than those not on drugs[4] – as their outcome depends on the severity of the disorder, the coping skills of the person and also on the expressed emotion (EE) level of the scenario they return to. Indeed, for patients in low EE homes the benefits of medication at all over the first nine months are debateable;[5] in high EE homes medication confers no advantages after two years;[6] and for patients on medication-only treatment, with no or minimal psychosocial help, the relapse rates are invariably very high.[7] The general success of patients who have never taken, or who have stopped, medication is also vastly understated in the medical psychiatric literature[8] – and one suspects that this observation is submerged under a mountain of drug company money.

It is clear that, in general, both biological and psychological help needs to be available for sufferers of paranoia and schizophrenia.[9] The relative balance and combination of the two must be determined by the real individual *needs* of the sufferer; but *neither* biological nor psychological help should be forced on the person (unless they are a danger to themselves or others) as the single answer to their problems.

In the introduction to this book I said that we have regarded psychotics as 'holes in theoretical space', to be jogged around by genetic, biochemical and social and community factors. Now the effects of that tendency are taking hold. Research is accumulating to the effect that even reducing the expressed emotion level of the home may in some cases only *delay* relapse in patients, rather than eliminating it.[10] Even when helped by a reduction in the EE level of their homes, the real-life adjustment of non-relapsing patients still remains marginal.[11] It could well be that this is because the actual interpretative and psychological skills of the sufferer, at the level of the individual patient, and taking their own world of meaning and personal view of life into account, have not been addressed.[12] It is simply not sufficient to juggle external factors around in the hope of being therapeutic, regarding the sufferer as having a 'condition' that has to be 'managed' (as, for example, in[13]) without intimately discussing the patient's personal experience and view of the world and their relationships. This neglect of the meaning of the sufferer's experiences, the so-called 'phenomenological' level of analysis,[14] may well be resulting in the 'revolving-door pattern' that psychotic patients tend to produce.

Do families cause schizophrenia and paranoia?

This is the 'sixty-four thousand dollar' question to which all families want an answer. Are families to blame?

One answer to this (the one I personally prefer) is that *nobody* is to blame for schizophrenia and paranoia and that such psychoses are basically caused by *life*, with all that that entails. But another possible answer is: in some cases, in part – yes.

It is exceedingly strange that recovering patients have a higher rate of relapse after returning to some types of family than others.[15] These families themselves have become highly suspicious about the mixed messages which tell them that they might cause their offspring's relapse if they don't change – but have nothing at all to do with the original onset of the illness.[16] How can this be? It makes *no psychological* sense at all (we are not dealing here with a broken leg) and in their hearts families know it. This issue confronts us with a (purely political) manoeuvre to maintain the image of psychosis as wholly and completely caused by genetic and biochemical factors: thus ensuring it is fully within the realm of biological and positivist science, with its chemical and behavioural solutions and the finances that back them.[17] It is no coincidence that family management programmes are singularly non-psychological in content, as this is a research effort from 'brain and behavioural science' not psychology and social science. The inner life of the patient is not addressed, which is certainly an omission; the absurdity of it sometimes rising to bizarre levels (for example,[18]) in these programmes.

Nonetheless, one has to take the broad picture of causal factors as a whole. Although deviant communication and high expressed emotion or EE (over-involvement and high criti-

cism), together with other processes such as over-talkative-
ness and high guilt induction, have been seriously implicated
as causal factors in schizophrenia,[19] it is important to remember, however, that 50% of schizophrenic patients come from
low expressed emotion homes.[20] We know now that a
family's high EE is not simply a reaction to the patient's own
challenging and disturbing behaviour;[21] nevertheless it is
essential to recognize that the psychological effect of a relationship is an interactive product to some degree – people
do behave in different ways with different people, so the

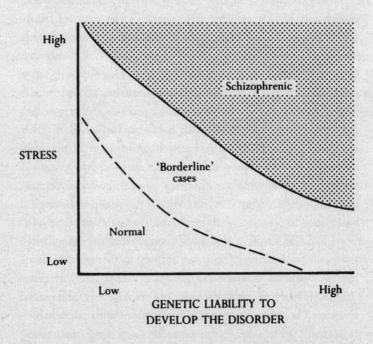

GENETIC LIABILITY TO
DEVELOP THE DISORDER

The higher the person's genetic liability to develop psychosis, the lower the stress
from environmental sources necessary to trigger it — and vice versa. This figure
leaves out the 'coping ability' of the person, which probably relates strongly to
intelligence and which adds another dimension to the story.

apportioning of blame for madness is really a meaningless exercise. In addition, the degree of genetic predisposition to psychosis varies from person to person, so the role of environmental factors in tipping the scales at the 'madness threshold' also varies from person to person (see Figure 1).[22] For some people environmental factors, such as family processes, play a negligible role, but in less vulnerable people (who therefore need more 'environmental push') they may be huge.

For me, one of the most distressing features of my work on madness over the years has been to see what terrible scenarios people can get themselves into with *time*. 'How did we get into this mess?' they ask despairingly. There is no doubt that some relationships weaken both or all of the people in them; other relationships strengthen everyone. But which way a relationship goes one can never, and perhaps never will be able, to tell. Relationships are adventures, not experiments, and adventures can easily go badly wrong. In my experience the worst scenario that can evolve is that of a patronizing over-protective, over-involved person with a supposed inept dependant of some kind. These scenarios evolve into what they are over the years, sometimes decades, through a million jolts and jogs where no one (really) is to blame; but when one meets them 'fully developed', if such a phrase can be used here, they can be ugly in the extreme.[23]

Most researchers now agree that the most critical damaging feature of those families that are high EE (and this, remember, is by no means all) is undoubtedly this *over-involvement*[24], which also turns out to be exceedingly resistant to all efforts to change it.[25] I have met many psychotic patients who have pointed to this particular factor as one of the key processes that, as one girl put it, 'softened them up for madness' (although even here they do tend to admit that they also had a predisposition or were 'not really right anyway'). However, it is important to recognize that over-involvement also occurs in romantic relationships, not only in families (and even in friendships and work relationships); so in some cases it is the over-involvement of partners, friends and spouses, not mothers or fathers, which is the problem. (In some respects, researchers, like their patients, are a little too fixated on the home and just will not leave it.)[26]

Why is over-involvement so terribly damaging? The central characteristics of over-involved people are that they have come, one way or another, to see themselves as vastly *superior* and more competent in life than the people they are involved with, but at the same time they are desperately dependent on them for their existence. To avoid using the term 'parent', because this does not always apply, I will say that they are the psychic equivalent of a huge planet (say Jupiter), be this husband, mother, friend or whatever, with a satellite (say Ganymede) who is the illness sufferer, or soon will be, operating in mutual parasitic dependence. But here, unlike in the solar system, Jupiter cannot let Ganymede go or else Jupiter might wither away to nothing: because here it is usually the case that Jupiter has come to a point or period in their lives when they have nothing else to live for *but* Ganymede.

Over-involved parents and partners always present themselves as doting, harmless, loving, devoted people, whose first thought is always for the good of their 'satellite'. In fact, this can sometimes be a half-truth and at worst it can be a sham. The negative side is revealed starkly when the satellite tries to break away and assert its own identity, and build up its own individual life and existence. For the psychological reality of their relationship is that Jupiter cannot *survive* without the downward comparison provided by the tiny helpless Ganymede. If Ganymede grows up, or becomes fit for independent life, Jupiter is *finished*. It is an appalling scenario.

The Jupiter–Ganymede syndrome is sad, pathetic and tragic. Living with an over-involved parent, for example, when you're really starting to grow up, is like being relentlessly pursued by an arrogant lover you don't at all want but who will *not* get it through their head that you *can* manage perfectly well on your own. And of course they *will* keep on picking up on every tiny shred of 'evidence' that they can find that you are somehow incompetent, do indeed desperately need them and 'can't live without them'. This is enough to drive many people to distraction. The consequences are humiliating, denigrating, degrading, infantilizing, and, in some cases, can even be basically violent and hateful. The total effect is to deny another human being their right to live and to be, and to have their own opinions and way of existing, in the service of inflating and preserving the Jupiter person's self-image and giving them something to do with a life (theirs) that they otherwise secretly perceive now, on its own, as worthless.

Jupiters have to keep their Ganymedes *down*, or else the power balance of the relationship would be undermined. So the defences of criticism and humiliation are often also used by these 'loving, harmless, caring' people to remind their Ganymedes how helpless and needy they are and how they 'obviously' cannot get by in life on their own. It is hardly surprising that the Ganymedes' self-worth and sense of personal *control* is low and that their minds are squeezed into nothingness by these 'doting, devoted' individuals.

But, when all is said and done, Jupiter-type individuals are in themselves extremely sad people. In most cases they are more frightened of Ganymede's escape than angry and hateful about it. Although it is indeed horrific to see the fetid violence of a very aggressive Jupiter spitting and sneering at their escaping satellite (as I have seen); it is also horrific to see the more fearful Jupiters slide into alcoholism (as I have also seen), commit suicide (usually romantic partners), sob with tears flooding from the very depths of their being, or simply fade away and die on Ganymede's escape. Jupiters are actually tragic people who need help, and sometimes *far more help* than their satellites: although it is always the berated satellite that ends up in the psychiatric unit and which we are asked to 'treat'. (But I fear, not treat so effectively that they really do become independent.)

The implicit psychological violence of the Jupiter–Ganymede syndrome has a lot to do with the flowering of madness in some people. It is a no-gain 'heads I win, tails you lose' scenario (which poses as 'protectiveness'), when the *only* final escape is into psychosis; but it is not an escape that does anyone much good (although it might feasibly inflate some Jupiters to even greater size).

One behavioural solution to this problem is simply to cut down the number of contact hours per week between Ganymedes and Jupiters[27] (where this is possible); but this does nothing to change the essential psychological dynamics of the relationships, so the effects could hardly be expected to be lasting or permanent. The real answer to this problem is to work intensively on the co-dependence of these people and help the Jupiters to enlarge their own life's radius[28] as well as helping the Ganymedes to trust in their own decisions and judgement. In work of this kind the motivations of the people concerned have to be faced; it is no use merely rearranging daily work and activity schedules to give a superficial independence. However, cognitive–behavioural interventions which are focused specifically on helping the Ganymede's feelings of self-worth, and on helping them to be more self-confident and *self-reliant*, might be helpful in situations where the Jupiters *have no role at all* and hence can never 'oversee' activities (to 'check whether everything is all right' etc.).

Generally I would say that it is exceedingly unwise to return previously psychotic deluded patients, after they have left hospital, to relationships where serious over-involvement is detected. Revulsion at the humiliating dependency of these relationships plays a part in the paranoid fear-of-dependency which can be triggered off as a reaction. Such relationships are not beneficial to either of the parties in them. In truth, the bond is better severed and the parties then supported so as to re-establish a real life for each. The critical issues to focus on are the enhancement of self-worth, self-confidence and the sense of individual *identity* in both patient and partner: only then can they stand up inside and become a real living person in their own right. But Jupiters must themselves also be brave and strong enough to show that they are *willing* to let go and that their Ganymede's thrust for life *has their assent*.

Isolation and withdrawal

It is well recognized that manic patients go out to meet stimulation and are very open to social relationships, while paranoid, schizoid and schizophrenic people tend to withdraw and close in on themselves.[29] This is probably partly rooted in temperamental differences, such as their basic levels of extroversion and introversion, which are heavily genetically loaded;[30] but withdrawal also has to be seen as a reaction to

circumstances, to inner feelings and to one's interpretation of
life. Hence it also depends not only on 'automatic' processes
but on 'control' processes.

There are several causes and consequences of withdrawal
which I have outlined below in five simple points: these are
likely to operate in a kind of circular causality fashion, each
reinforcing itself and the others. If sufferers, family and
friends have some insight into the reasons for and the effects
of withdrawal, this may help all to cope.

1. The fewer people a person sees and talks to
    intimately, the less chance there is of *testing* and
    checking their ideas against everyday shared reality.[31]
    Other people jolt and jog our thinking so that it
    usually becomes, in essence, more effective, efficient
    and functional and so that it helps us to get by in life
    better. Many bizarre systems of thought therefore
    don't get a hold on people in everyday life because,
    as the saying goes, 'laughter prevented it'. Cut
    yourself off from people and all that you will know is
    your own world; you won't benefit from checks and
    refutations – or indeed laughter. This is the negative
    side of withdrawal.

2. Withdrawal often occurs, however, because a person
    feels they have sensed or conceived a deep truth that
    their immediate contacts would never recognize or
    appreciate – and they feel that they have to develop
    their thinking to see where it leads. Many writers,
    artists, philosophers and scientists, of course, come
    into this category. Solitude may be necessary for
    outstanding creativity. Einstein himself was almost
    'incommunicado' during his time at the Princeton

Advanced Study Centre, when he was immersed in the problems and paradoxes of quantum theory. This is the positive side of withdrawal.

3. If a person feels stressed, agitated and troubled by the *kinds* of thoughts and feelings they are having, social interaction and stimulation may make them feel worse. Their own thinking may embarrass, frighten and alienate them. Because of its sheer *intensity*, stimulation also affects how we feel — positive or negative — so withdrawal can be an attempt to modulate our felt arousal and stress. (This is actually the Eysenckian view of extroversion and introversion.)[32] We go out and go into ourselves, as we feel we need to, to adjust the tone of our experiences. Even extroverts therefore sometimes withdraw. This is the functional side of withdrawal.

4. Schizoid and many paranoid people feel that they are somehow 'stood back inside'. This is the experience of not really feeling in touch or at one with social life, of somehow looking out at it as if through a tunnel where it has to be analysed and 'computed' rather than directly sensed and felt. (Laing once spoke of a schizoid patient who could not have intercourse with his girlfriend unless he simultaneously *fantasized* about having intercourse with her.) It may indeed be that schizoid distant people, such as Newton and John Stuart Mill, had their analytical skills because they needed them. Powers of analysis may genetically 'go with' a schizoid temperament to aid the person's survival. The trouble is that their skills do not lend themselves to smooth social functioning (unless conversation — as it often is in

universities – is continually bent around to an
analytical mode). The result is that such people are
said not to 'mesh' well with others and they are
often seen as odd or eccentric, or lacking tact and
common sense at an everyday level. Social
functioning, say at a party, needs the parallel
instantaneous processing of a *lot* of information from
many sources and analytical people, who generally
proceed in a step-by-step serial fashion with a
narrow 'beam of attention', just cannot handle these
scenarios. They are too difficult for them because
their brains are simply not geared to this kind of
activity. Give them a theorem to prove and they are
much better. People may withdraw, therefore, to
avoid situations which, in effect, frighten and
embarrass them. This is withdrawal due to 'negative
reinforcement'. The person becomes conditioned to
escape.

5. Psychotic and religious experiences (which, as we
   know, often go together) are strange and
   bewildering. In Western society we have next to no
   education about the mystical realm and about
   'cosmic consciousness', so if and when the mystical
   enters our experience we are utterly unprepared for
   it.[33] Because of this people may withdraw not
   because (or not only because) they are afraid to
   communicate, but because they *cannot* communicate
   what they are going through to family and friends.
   The experience is ineffable (indeed, at times,
   euphoric): the person experiencing it, literally, 'out
   of this world'. I was only able to understand seven
   years later what I had written myself in my diary at

the time of a mystical experience I had in 1979.
Mystical experiences, which are related to psychotic
experiences, are very very difficult indeed to share
properly.

These five aspects of withdrawal cover a great deal of the
variability involved in the factors that induce and maintain it.
Of course, in Western society we *value* extroverted behaviour very much more than introverted behaviour ('extroversion fascism') so we are more likely to see withdrawal as a
problem. (We might say, for example, 'Go and live in Liverpool for a year, it will take you out of yourself'. We never
say, 'Go and live near the desert for a year, it will send you
into yourself.'(!).) Psychiatric categories also never mention
such tendencies as 'sensorially fixated' or 'reality obsessed'.
No, it is the overvaluing of fantasy, not reality, which our
society tends to pathologize. Thus our culture has 'hang-ups'
about withdrawal which we would do well to be mindful of,
as we don't quite know how to react to it. A greater compassion for and understanding of the inner life – which will
come only to a limited degree from brain and behavioural
science – will do a great deal to ease the agonies of psychotic
people.

Paranoid and schizoid sensitivity

For all their social ineptness, paranoid people are well able to
discriminate sham emotional behaviour from the real thing.[34]
Schizoid people, rather than being dispositionally cold and
wooden, are also capable of immense sensitivity and
empathy, often alternating with brutal disinterest.[35]
Unfortunately, the great perceptiveness of paranoid

people is not combined with great flexibility of thought;[36] while non-paranoid people, including psychotics, are less sensitive but also less rigid.[37] The problem here is that increased agitation and alertness *also* makes thinking more rigid[38] whilst simultaneously focusing attention[39] at times onto minutiae. It is not surprising then that paranoid people are more aroused or 'revved up' than others.[40] If anything they are more driven by data and minutiae (which then feed their ideas), while non-paranoid and normal people are more driven by their ideas (which then lead them to find the data and the minutiae).[41] In other words: when psychotic people are considered, paranoids notice more than they can rationally handle, while non-paranoid deluded people tend to dream up more than they can justify.[42]

What effect does this have on *social* behaviour and relationships? It's not surprising that the effects are considerable. It is natural for people not to want to be read too closely, and it is not always the case that people who notice barely concealed subtleties in others simultaneously build up a total picture of their 'victim' which is fair and accurate. Close observational skill need not, and often does not, go with good broad judgement[43] – and can sometimes be distracting of attempts to grasp the whole. Although it can be said, with Laing, that the schizophrenic or schizophrenia-prone person is uncannily sensitive to the unconscious of others this tends to be to the 'negative unconscious' (rather in the Freudian style). The bulk of social life, however, is carried on at a relatively positive level and with a supportive style that the over-sensitive person has difficulty tuning into. Indeed, socially it is better simply to take people for what they seem to be[44] and present themselves as, since these qualities and procedures are uppermost in their minds anyway and generally guide their everyday behaviour most of the time.

Great sensitivity therefore has its disadvantages and, in being a threat in social life, the door is open for the person to be rejected and ostracized. This may indeed be felt to be unfair, and perhaps in a sense it is; but in a more important and profound sense it is not. Life could not have gone on, would not have been worth living, and society could not have evolved and survived as it has, were it not underpinned by a much deeper and broader set of *positive* impulses than are recognized in the Freudian negative unconscious. It is not surprising to find that altruism has a substantial genetic basis[45] and that people's judgements of others are consistently slanted towards the positive (actually and repeatedly in Greek 'golden section' proportions).[46] The vast bulk of humanity does *not* lie, steal and deceive, otherwise efficient social life and individual happiness would never obtain and the world of people would have disintegrated long ago. Paranoids are clever but not wise; they are deep, but not very deep.

The 'stood back inside' quality of paranoid and schizoid people may nonetheless be combined, as we saw earlier, with intense analytical skills. But analysis, like a television screen or a photograph, always puts a frame around that which it studies, amputates it from the whole and therefore inevitably distorts and misrepresents. Interestingly, psychologists are at last recognizing how analytical methods used in our own profession can easily under-estimate people and put them in a bad light.[47] Covering a whole territory with a hundred frames, and then adding the findings from these frames together, does not give the whole answer: this is what the poet Coleridge taught J.S. Mill – the whole has to be grasped intuitively. This is something that 'laser beam' minds just cannot ever grasp. As Mill did, paranoia-prone people would profit from more poetry.

Coping with a paranoid partner or relative

Hopefully the contents of this book will offer a number of ideas to help people in coping with paranoia in the home. However, in this section I will give an overview of the main strategies that need to be borne in mind when paranoid crises emerge, so as to spell out specifically what action is most useful and effective.

1.   The most critical coping method is preventative – it is important to try to foresee problems before they actually emerge in full measure. To give a couple of examples: some (if not all) important *life changes*, such as getting or losing a job, leaving home or returning to it, giving birth or suffering the loss of a loved one who has been ill for some time, to a certain extent can be foreseen. It is found that when people anticipate and imagine these very stressful events, and talk through alternative strategies of how they will cope, their impact is much reduced. Paranoia easily emerges under stress (for example, mixing with new people in the workplace) and abrupt changes and novel situations can produce such pressure. Many patients, who have been ill before, do actually show a pattern of behaviour – a 'relapse signature'[48] – which indicates that they are becoming unwell again and such patterns can be looked out for.

In other cases it is specific stressors, rather than general scenarios, that trigger paranoia. Money problems may be a weak spot or things going missing, or sexual relationships. An over-involved mother may fear being 'left alone to die' when her children leave home. So when they become old enough to start regular dating and sexual relationships, she may become paranoid that her offspring will be snatched away by an evil suitor or that they are eager to leave and are on the look-out for potential partners with whom to move in. Again, this problem, to a degree, can be foreseen, talked over and planned for. It is reassuring to know that even recognizing a potential stressor before it occurs is calming in itself, even if a perfect solution to the quandary cannot easily, or at first, be found.

2. It is important with paranoid people to be fair and respectful and not treat them as if they are totally stupid simply because their beliefs are different from yours. People who are paranoid about 'burglary plots' or about the activities of gossipy neighbours are rarely totally unrealistic given the vicissitudes of urban and suburban life. It is better to react with statements such as, 'I can appreciate that this is a worry but I am sure the reality is nowhere near as bad as you imagine', or 'These things do go on, you're right, but you may be making a mountain out of a molehill'. But continually to tell the person that they are talking 'utter nonsense' is humiliating, infuriating and never effective.

3. Management and recovery from paranoia has a lot to do with helping the person control their own thinking. Among mental health workers this is known as the development of 'metacognitive strategies'. Too many paranoid people simply go along with their thinking, taking the path of least resistance wherever it leads (even if it is to death's

door itself). Much of this book has been about aiding insight into the mistakes and biases in paranoid thought, so it is important that the topics I have raised be aired. Chronically paranoid people, however, have often been brought up to believe that other people are extremely cruel – and, given *this* cognition, a lot of the rest of their thinking makes a kind of sense. They are, therefore, on the look-out for the slightest evidence that their assumptions in this respect are true. 'Cognitive control' must, therefore, proceed in step with a relationship that is basically affectionate and caring. A paranoid person is not a computer to be reprogrammed, but a feeling, social being who will only become well in the company of fair and honest people who genuinely *like* them.

4. Most patients find it helpful (when it is suggested) to regard their beliefs as hypotheses or theories rather than 'facts'. They are really hypotheses based on *evidence* and hence it is useful to look very closely at this evidence with the sufferers and see if it could be reinterpreted in other ways. Chapter 3 gave a number of examples where the character puts spectacular (and cruel) interpretations onto mundane and innocent events. Regarding a paranoid belief as a construction, rather than a solid reality,[49] leaves the door ajar to assessment of the evidence; and it is there that actual dialogue can make real inroads into the problem.

5. It is best to be accepting that the person has the beliefs they have, and to be prepared to listen in detail to how they came to be formed, before

challenging them. Any challenge needs to be gentle and respectful; loud, dismissive, critical challenges usually make the person dig their heels in even more – and are damaging of their self-respect.

6. Make an effort to separate paranoid beliefs that could very well be true from those that are almost certainly false. It is dangerous to assume that *everything* a paranoid person says is wrong – it rarely is and such an attitude is a deadly barrier to communication and improvement.

7. Paranoia is often about something else rather than the surface delusion. It may be necessary to ask, 'What is *really* at the bottom of all this?'. The answer could be a guilty secret, a feeling that their partner doesn't love them any more, a feeling that really they hate the neighbourhood and 'should never have moved here' and so on. It is not true that all paranoids have a guilty conscience, at least not consciously, but nothing stimulates paranoia better than guilt interacting with fragmentary or unclear evidence. Talking over guilt feelings can be very beneficial.

8. Although it doesn't really address central problems: people do speak less about delusional beliefs if they are rewarded (by attention, smiles, etc.) for *non*-delusional talk.[50] However, 'punishment' for delusional talk is not therapeutic – it is far better to reward normal communication. Such methods, however, are only likely to be effective if the sufferer does not realize that they are being applied. This same approach can be applied to people who,

although not paranoid or quite deluded, talk incessantly and infuriatingly about some single issue or topic – such as money they (might) be entitled to or the evils of the local MP. These are known as 'over-valued ideas' and can actually precede a delusional episode. Therefore, regularly distracting the person onto other topics might itself be preventative of more serious developments.

9. Because many relatives and partners implicitly think that medicine and clinical psychology totally revolve around the sufferer of an illness they themselves do not seek any help. This attitude is quite wrong. We are now becoming acutely aware of the distress families undergo[51] and treatment teams are open to calls for help from family members or partners. Do consult your GP with a view to obtaining support; there may even be a family self-help group in your area for people in exactly your situation. Find out what resources are available. A social worker may also be able to visit and give advice on benefits, etc. if a partner's disorder is causing financial hardship. In addition to this, don't be averse to trying to get away for a few days. Continual exposure to a sick person is phenomenally draining of personal resources. What-ever you do, *don't* just sit there suffering in silence.

10. If the sick person requires professional help, it is far better if all interested parties work together as a team and share ideas, experiences and information. It is also better for families to be knowledgeable about their member's illness, as the feeling of knowledge eases stress and prevents strong shock and surprise reactions when the otherwise 'unheard-of' occurs.

11. Finally, do not yourself be 'sucked into' the ill person's beliefs. Accept that they have certain ideas but stand firm and assert that you do not share them.[52]

7

CONCLUSIONS AND IMPLICATIONS FOR THE FUTURE

This final chapter will be relatively brief and succinct. It should be fairly clear from the earlier chapters, particularly Chapter 3, that we can no longer afford to ignore what sufferers of serious mental illness have to say – their story from within.[1] We have to listen to their experience, find the sense and meaning in it, and draw compassion and under-standing from our knowledge of our own latent insanity.

We have also to recognize that people go insane partly because of the nature of their journey through life, because of what they've brought out of others – and what others have brought out of them, their latent derangement and despair. We have to start realizing that insanity is not mere senselessness[2] and stupidity: it is a way of making sense out of life, given the resources and biases that the person possesses. We must face that it is dormant in us *all*, that the sane and the insane are brothers and sisters. We have to acknowledge the positive side of psychosis, its creative aspect, the way it may help to enhance a person's spiritual sensitivities, open new doors of perception and insight, and bring humility and tenderheartedness.

In our culture even the words 'problem' and 'disturbance' are pejorative but they can be construed or 'reframed' in a positive way.³ What we have to recognize is that disturbance is inevitable in a growing adapting organism, meeting the demands of a life where the only certainties are change and death. As for problems, Nietzsche had this to say: 'Another problem? . . . Hooray!'.

In the past we have been embarrassed about illness (particularly mental illness) and sought refuge in the ministrations of doctors. But now we realize that there can never be enough professionals to go around. We must, to some degree, take our health into our own hands. When it comes to insanity we have to recognize that this is also the responsibility of the community, of the world. It is not something to be laid only at the door of geneticists and biochemists. It is impossible to have a totally intrapsychic understanding of paranoia and schizophrenia because they are also partly social and spiritual phenomena.

Given that this is the case, we must also realize that disturbed patients are not at all predictable — because what they do, including violent acts, does not spring entirely from their own heads. Their actions can depend on a chance *social* event such as seeing a 'meaningful' newspaper headline, seeing someone on the bus tighten their tie ('is this symbolic or "a sign"?'), or seeing someone inadvertently smirk (in fact, at a memory that's just come into their mind). All manner of transient events, when the 'meaning feeling' is upon a person, can seem sinister and portentous — as indeed, for them, they are. The failure of psychiatrists to anticipate outrageous acts from discharged patients is therefore perfectly understandable. Only an all-knowing God could predict such acts.

It is vitally important that we support research that refers to the sufferers' own thoughts and feelings. We need this to build an adequate theory on which to base solid intervention efforts. This is the kind of research that the sufferer can also relate to, understand, digest and eventually use at an every-day level to help manage their *own* thinking and perceiving. Chemical formulae mean nothing to most recovering psychotic people, or to those who are prone to psychosis. Indeed they can seem so alien that the people who take the tablets they describe can feel that their destiny no longer lies in their own hands at all. This, of course, has been the very experience they had when they were ill.

In this book I have spoken of paranoid psychoses, paranoid personality disorder and schizophrenia etc. as *illnesses*. My own personal view is that the extraordinary facility with which all manner of impressions, events, ideas, statements and occurrences of all kinds are taken to 'fit' or 'confirm' a person's evolving delusional system does reflect a real malfunction in the brain. (Indeed, on a technical note, I am sure this 'hyperaccess' problem could be modelled by artificial intelligence researchers on a connectionist neural network, as these are particularly powerful at pattern recognition itself.[4]) There is, I am sure, real organic disorder beneath the experience of madness. Hence by intention (or by default) we could in the future build psychotic machines, a disturbing thought to con-template. However, whether the person suffering from psychotic paranoia could be said to 'have a disease' is another matter and on this, except in a few extreme cases, I would have to dissent. These illnesses do not follow the inexorable course of a disease process.[5] Madness is partly an accelerated and inflated capacity to detect 'relevant' patterns. But this tendency is inherent in all organisms (who might therefore – even plants – suffer a limited form of 'psychosis' of a kind) and it is also the very foundation of all perception and creativity. This is why creativity and madness are so often allied – although real, socially useful, creativity tends to precede insanity rather than follow it.

The actual presence of *illness* does not, however, necessarily imply disease, as the latter has numerous implications which do not apply to the conditions discussed here.[6] In contrast, psychosis is the triggering of an orchestra of processes that, with different events and in different circumstances, could have been socially and personally useful (or at least neutral) rather than damaging.[7] The genetic disengaging of the biological potential for paranoid and schizophrenic insanity, if this is ever done, will at the same time disengage much that is essential, poetic and beautiful in our world. We are therefore approaching some exceedingly dangerous choices in the prevention of mental disorder.[8]

Some readers may feel that I have said some rather disparaging things about the families of psychotic people in these pages. For some families my remarks are appropriate, but I have tried to make clear that for others they are not. Rather than being over-involved, there are many families who would prefer to see *less* of their disturbed offspring, not more. There are still others who hold this latter attitude, yet who are still patronizing and damaging when they *do* see him or her. Still others are not over-involved or patronizing in any way, and yet others who, while low in EE, actually reinforce withdrawal,[9] sometimes to a detrimental degree. Clearly there can be no valid generalization about the families of paranoia and schizophrenia sufferers. As I have said before, there are 'many roads to Rome' and for some people pathological family processes are *not* to be found along any of them. In the end, assessments have to be made at an individual level and we must remember that we are dealing with people – not cases – every one of them unique.[10]

Although we have so far recognized it largely in human beings, it could be that psychosis is a feature of the entire organic world. In creative work, particularly painting and poetry, enhanced pattern detection and construction can be wonderfully functional. It is hardly surprising that artistic work, or rather play, can be a productive and positive way for recovering psychotic clients to take.[11]

One of the problems for both the artist and the psychotic, however, is that both, particularly in the twentieth century, are 'punished for poetry' unless they are truly astounding. Artists fully recognize that man can believe the impossible, but never believe the merely improbable (Oscar Wilde). Psychotics are no different from 'standard' people in seeking certainty even in the impossible. This facility is a particular and curious quirk of the human mind. The mind does not just adapt to reality for survival purposes, or even create a new world, as Western society has done; it revels in the creation of impossibilities – some of which we may strive to realize, some we can never realize. This quintessentially human tendency is in many ways the positive side of paranoia and delusional thinking: and yet it is a form of thinking for which Dali and Magritte,[12] at least, were rewarded but for which so many are chastized.

The creations of psychotics are art not science; they are of the irrational not the rational, Dionysian rather than Apollonian. The psychotic's mistake is to take them for truth when, in fact, they are of the world of the dream (Dali was self-critical enough to realize this).

The 'impossible' is territory where reason cannot go. Poets of word or brush, such as Blake, Keats, Malevich and Wilde, regularly trod there and returned enriched and able to enrich the rest of us. Many have found themselves through immersion in the work of these artists. Access to the 'impossible' puts the possible in perspective, and gives the individual an horizon to steer by.

But, as physicists never cease to tell us, reality is weird.[13]

It may yet be found that our 'impossible' creations are nearer to 'deep truth'[14] than all the elegancies of reason. It may sound like the talk of madmen, yet it may still be better to ask how science is possible in a reality that is essentially poetic, rather than: has poetry any place in a world totally characterized by science?

Research on paranoia and schizophrenia has its own conflicts, professional rivalries and entrenched views.[15] Researchers may even give the same mixed messages and deviant communications as the families they are treating or helping.[16] Cognitive biases also occur in psychotherapists,[17] and in doctors and research scientists,[18] as well as psychotics. Life is messy and unfair. But eventually things do get done. It is my hope that a genuine *team* approach, involving both biological and social science, artists as well as scientists, diagnosticians as well as process researchers and the religious as well as the agnostic, will be brought to bear with time on the understanding of the psychotic mind. If we heal our own divisions, and recognize each other's contributions, the path will be clearer for a genuine unified multidisciplinary assault on one of the greatest enigmas of the universe – madness.

APPENDIX

Suggestions for further reading

As I said at the outset, many works on serious mental disorders, including paranoia and schizophrenia are dry and mechanistic. There are a few texts, however, which combine academic excellence with a warm insightful attitude and which are written both exceptionally clearly and with real vitality and vigour. These books I would recommend. Most of their titles are self explanatory. (The final one listed is on irrationality in general rather than on psychosis.)

Richard Bentall, 1990. *Reconstructing Schizophrenia*.London, Routledge. (A book that comes close to *de*constructing 'schizophrenia' out of existence as a useful concept and certainly as a unitary entity.)

Peter Breggin, 1993. *Toxic Psychiatry*. London, Fontana. (A strong anti-drugs stance, but very one-sided.)

Anthony Clare, 1980. *Psychiatry in Dissent*. London, Tavistock.

Gordon Claridge, 1985. *Origins of Mental Illness*. Oxford, Blackwell.

Anthony Storr, 1972. *The Dynamics of Creation*. London, Secker and Warburg. (The *why* rather than the *how* of creativity.)

Stuart Sutherland, 1976. *Breakdown*. London, Weidenfeld. (His own experience of manic-depressive illness and a sketch coverage of theory and treatment in the field of psychopathology.)

Stuart Sutherland, 1993. *Irrationality*. London, Constable. (Entertaining overview of biases, illusions and delusions of perfectly sane people.)

My own previous book *Borderline*, first published by Routledge in 1992, combines insights from my own experience of a paranoid illness (which overwhelmed me in 1979) with work on a number of other people's experiences and with suggestions for improving the practice of therapy. The general presentation is reader-friendly, although the section in the middle of the book – dealing with my experimental work on paranoia and delusional thinking – is rather technical.

USEFUL ADDRESSES AND TELEPHONE NUMBERS

Great Britain
MIND
Grantha House
15–19 Broadway
Stratford
London E15 4BQ
Helpline: 0181-519 2122

National Schizophrenia Fellowship (NSF)
28 Castle Street
Kingston-on-Thames
Surrey KT1 1SS
National Office telephone: 0181-547 3937
Comprehensive advice service: 0181-974 6814
(A police training video is available from NSF)

SANE (Schizophrenia, A National Emergency)
199–205 Old Marylebone Road
London NW1 5QP
Saneline (2pm to midnight every day of the year, including Bank
Holidays and Christmas Day)
: 0171-724 8000 : 0345-67 8000
(These numbers service the whole of Great Britain.)
Main office telephone number: 0171-724 6520

The Mental Aftercare Association
25 Bedford Square
London WC1B 3HW
Tel.: 0171-436 6194

The Mental Health Foundation
37 Mortimer Street
London W1N 7RJ
Tel: 0171-580 0145

The Schizophrenia Association of Great Britain
Bryn Hyfryd
The Crescent
Bangor
Gwynedd LL57 2AG
Wales
Tel: 01248-354048

User groups, support and advocacy
Survivors Speak Out
The Diorama
34 Osnaburgh Street
London NW1 3ND
Tel.: 0171-916 6991

Turning Point
Newloom House
101 Blackchurch Lane
London E1 1LU
Tel.: 0171-702 2300

Specialized organizations which include mental health
Alzheimer's Disease Society
158–160 Balham High Road
London SW12 9BN
Tel.: 0181-675 6557

Age Concern England
Astral House
1268 London Road
London SW16 4ER
Tel.: 0181-679 8000

Samaritans
Tel.: 0753-532 713
London.: 0171-734 2800

Shelter
88 Old Street
London EC1V 9HU
England
Tel.: 0171-253 0202

Medical organizations concerned with mental health
Mental Health Foundation
37 Mortimer Street
London W1N 7RJ
Tel: 0171-580 0145

British Medical Association
Tavistock Square
London WC1H 9JP
Tel.: 0171-387 4499

Institute of Psychiatry
De Crespigny Park
Denmark Hill
London SE5 8AF
Tel.: 0171-703 5411

The King's Fund Centre
126 Albert Street
London NW1 7NF
Tel.: 0171-267 6111

Royal College of Psychiatrists
17 Belgrave Square
London SW1X 8PG
Tel.: 0171-235 2351

Organizations concerned with the mental health of ethnic communities

Afro-Caribbean Mental Health Association
35 Electric Avenue
London SW9
Tel.: 0171-737 3603

Commission for Racial Equality
Eliot House
10/12 Allington Street
London SW1E 5EH
Tel.: 0171-828 7022

Confederation of Indian Organizations
5 Westminster Bridge Road
London SE1 7XW
Tel.: 0171-928 9889

Mental health and Social Security

Department of Social Security
The Adelphi
1–11 John Adam Street
London WC2N 6HT
Tel.: 0171-962 8000
0771-883300 *(DWA Enquiry Line)*
0345-123456 *(DLA Enquiry Line)*

The Benefits Agency
Chief Executive's Office
Room 4CO6
Quarry House
Quarry Hill

Leeds LS2 7UA
Tel.: 0800-882200
Benefits Enquiry Line (0800-243355 Textphone)

Disability Alliance
Universal House
88–94 Wentworth Street
London E1 7SA
Tel.: 0171-247 8763 *Rights Line*
Tel.: 0171-247 8776 *Office Line*

United States
AMI/FAMI (Alliance for the Mentally Ill and the Friends and Advocates
of the Mentally Ill)
432 Park Avenue South
Suite 710
New York NY 10016-8806
Tel.: (0101) 212 684 3264 (FAMI)
For *information* also dial 1-800-950-NAMI

Schizophrenia Foundation of New York
Fryer Research Centre
105 East 22nd Street
Suite 809
New York NY 10010
Tel.: (0101) 212 473 5100

and

30 East 40th Street
Suite 608
New York NY 10016
Tel.: (0101) 212 808 4940

Washington D.C. Association of Mental Illness Services
can be contacted on:
(0101) 202 265 6363
or
(0101) 202 328 9470

The Washington D.C. Institute of Mental Hygiene is on:
(0101) 202 232 5454

The National Institute of Mental Health
5600 Fishers Lane
Room 15C-05
Rockville
MD 20857

National Mental Health Associations Inc.
2101 Wilson Blvd. Suite 302
Arlington, VA 22201

American Schizophrenia Association (ASA)
900 N. Federal Hwy.,
Boca Raton, FL 33432
Tel.: 1-800 847 3802
or:
    305 393 6167

Anxiety Disorders Association of America
6000 Executive Blvd.
Suite 200
Rockville, MD 20852-4004

National Depressive and Manic-Depressive Association
730 N. Franklin
Suite 501
Chicago
Il. 60601

Australia
The New South Wales Association for Mental Health
Gladesville
Sydney
Tel.: (010) 612 816 1611

The Victorian Schizophrenia Fellowship
Fitzroy North
Melbourne
Tel.: (010) 613 482 4199

Denmark

SIND
L.I. Brandes Alle 4
1956 Frederiksberg
Copenhagen
Tel.: (45) 31 35 42 66

India

SCARF
C-46 13th Street
East Ana Nagar
Madras 600 102
Tel.: Madras 662697 *or* 617971

REFERENCES AND NOTES

Chapter 1

1. Meyer, Robert G. and Salmon, P., 1984. *Abnormal Psychology*. Allyn and Bacon Inc. pp. 219-22.
2. Baron-Cohen, S. Leslie, A.M. and Frith, W., 1985. Does the autistic child have 'a theory of mind'? *Cognition*, vol. 21, pp. 37-46.
3. Chadwick, P.K., 1988. *A psychological study of paranoia and delusional thinking*. Doctorate dissertation, Royal Holloway and Bedford New College, University of London, p. 303.
4. Harper, D.J., 1992. Defining delusion and the serving of professional interests. The case of 'paranoia'. *British Journal of Medical Psychology*, vol. 65, pp. 357-69.
5. Bentall, R.P., 1990. *The syndromes and symptoms of psychosis (or why you can't play 'twenty questions' with the concept of schizophrenia and hope to win)*. In R.P. Bentall (ed) *Reconstructing Schizophrenia*. Routledge, London. p. 30.
6. Oltmanns, T.F., 1988. *Approaches to the definition and study of delusions*. In T.F. Oltmanns and B.A. Maher *Delusional Beliefs*. Chichester, John Wiley, p. 5.
7. Manschreck, T.C., 1979. The assessment of paranoid features. *Comparative Psychiatry*, vol. 20, pp. 370-77.
8. Jaspers, K., 1963. *General Psychopathology* (H.J. Hoenig and M.W. Hamilton, Trans.) University of Chicago Press.
9. The categories discussed here are taken from the *Diagnostic and*

Statistical Manual of the American Psychiatric Association (DSM IIIR 1987 and DSM IV 1994)., Washington D.C.

10. Murphy, H.B.M., 1983. Sociocultural variations in symptomatology, incidence and course of illness. *In* M. Shepherd and O.L. Sangwill. (eds.) *Handbook of Psychiatry vol. 1: General Psychopathology.* Cambridge, Cambridge University Press.

11. See a number of discussions of this in my own book *Borderline*, London, Routledge, 1992.

12. For a recent overview of personality disorders, see Peter Tyrer and George Stein *Personality Disorder Reviewed.* 1993, Gaskell.

13. Winters, K.C. and Neale. J.M., 1983. Delusions and delusional thinking in psychotics: A review of the literature. *Clinical Psychology Review*, vol. 3, no. 2, pp. 227-53.

14. Choi, P.Y.L., 1993. Alarming Effects of Anabolic Steroids. *The Psychologist*, vol. 6, No. 6, June, pp. 258-60.

15. Zimbardo, P.G., Andersen, S.M. and Kabat, I.G. 1981. Induced hearing deficit generates experimental paranoia. *Science* vol. 212, pp. 1529-31.

   See also:

   Hammeke, T.A., McQuillen, M.P. and Cohen, B.A., 1983. Musical hallucinations associated with acquired deafness. *Journal of Neurology, Neurosurgery and Psychiatry*, vol. 46, pp. 570-72.

Chapter 2

1. Sagan, C., 1977. *The Dragons of Eden. Speculations on the evolution of human intelligence.* Sevenoaks, Hodder and Stoughton, p. 181.

2. Orford, J., 1992. *Community Psychology, Theory and Practice.* Chichester, John Wiley.

3. Cooper, C., and Kline, P. 1986. An evaluation of the Defence Mechanism Test. *British Journal of Psychology*, vol. 77, pp. 19-31.

4. Holmes, D.S., 1981. Existence of classical projection and the stress-reducing function of attributive projection: A reply to Sherwood. *Psychological Bulletin*, Vol. 90(3), pp. 460-6.

5. Freud, S., 1911. Psychoanalytic notes on an autobiographical account of a case of paranoia (dementia paranoides). *Standard Edition* vol. 12. London, Hogarth Press, pp. 3-82.

6.   Fenichel, D., 1946. *The Psychoanalytical Theory of Neurosis*, London, Routledge.

7.   Bonime, W., 1979. Paranoid Psychodynamics. *Contemporary Psychoanalysis*, vol. 15 (4) pp. 514-27.

8.   Maher, B.A., 1979. Delusional thinking and perceptual disorder. *Journal of Individual Psychology*, vol. 30, pp. 98-113.

9.   Zimbardo, P.G. Andersen, S.M, and Kabat, L.G., 1981. Induced hearing deficit generates experimental paranoia, *Science*, vol. 212, pp. 1529-31.

10. Zigler, E and Glick, M., 1988. Is paranoid schizophrenia really camouflaged depression? *American Psychologist*, vol. 43, pp. 284-90.

11. Kaney, S and Bentall, R.P., 1989. Persecutory delusions and attributional style. *British Journal of Medical Psychology*, vol. 62, pp. 191-8.

12. Chadwick, P. K., 1992. *Borderline: A psychological study of paranoia and delusional thinking*. London, Routledge.

13. Knight, R.P., 1940. The relationship of latent homosexuality to the mechanism of paranoid delusions. *Bulletin of the Menninger Clinic*, vol. 4, pp. 149-159.

14. Weiner, B., 1986. *An Attributional Theory of Motivation and Emotion*. Berlin, Heidelberg, Springer Verlag.

15. Colby, K.M., 1981. Modelling a paranoid mind. *Behavioural and Brain Sciences*, vol. 4, pp. 515-60.

16. Davison, G.C., and Neale, J.M. 1986. *Abnormal Psychology*, New York, Wiley.

17. Brown, G and colleagues, 1966. *Schizophrenia and Social Care*. Oxford, Oxford University Press.

18. Vaughn, C.E. and Leff, J.P., 1976. The influence of family and social factors on the course of psychiatric illness. *British Journal of Psychiatry*, vol. 129, pp. 125-137.

19. Claridge, G., 1985. *Origins of Mental Illness*. Oxford, Blackwell.

20. Wason, P., 1971. Problem solving and reasoning. *British Medical Bulletin*, vol. 27, pp. 206-10.

21. Wason, P. and Johnson-Laird, P., 1972 *Psychology of Reasoning*, Cambridge, Mass., Harvard University Press.

Chapter 3

1.   Meuris, Jacques, 1992. *René Magritte*. Taschen.

2. The heavy smoking of paranoid and deluded patients, especially those who are schizophrenic or suffering schizophrenia-like illness, is well known to professionals. A colleague of mine (Keith Laws) found that, in a sample of eighty schizophrenic patients he was testing at Charing Cross Hospital in London, only *one* was a non-smoker (personal communication, 1991). This almost one-to-one association of tobacco smoking and schizophrenia does not apply to the best of my knowledge in *any* other disorder, even in anxiety disorders and depression where distress is also very high. It is a curious association that may throw light on the causes of this family of illnesses. In my own doctorate thesis, in 1988, I reported that smokers were significantly higher in average pulse rate than non-smokers (75 beats per minute compared to 72), were more paranoid, more neurotic and more empathic in *disposition* than non-smokers and were significantly more rigid in their thinking. They were, however, *less* aggressive, depressed and anxious in their actual reported *mood* at the time of testing and felt more pleasant than non-smokers. It seems likely that paranoid and neurotic people smoke sporadically to ease their distress (hence the effects on mood). But there are reasons to believe that the increased physiological arousal produced by smoking (as I found from the pulse rate data) may well increase rigidity of thought and this, of course, could actually facilitate further paranoia. This possibility that tobacco smoking, usually used to placate distress, might actually act back as a risk factor for psychosis was also voiced by McManus and Weeks (1982) in *Psychological Medicine* (vol. 12, pp. 349-56). Another factor involved, however, is that tobacco smoking might subjectively ease schizophrenic patients' attentional and concentration difficulties (although the reality here is that it probably enhances hour after hour *persistence* rather than moment by moment concentration). This whole topic, however, is clearly an area deserving of considerable further research.

3. An imbalance in psychosis in the activity levels of the two hemispheres of the brain has been suggested by many authors over the last ten years or so. Paranoid and schizoid people tend to be analytical, close-focused and step-by-step or 'serial' in their thinking. They also tend to have great difficulty dealing with a lot of information coming at them all at once – so-called 'parallel processing'. This is consistent

with a model arguing for overactivation of the left hemisphere and underactivation of the right. When induced in normal volunteers, such a pattern also produces perseverance of belief and resistance to disconfirmatory information (see R. Drake and B. Bingham, *Brain and Cognition*, vol. 4, pp. 156-64). The case for this pattern is made in detail in my book *Borderline* (Routledge, 1992).

4. Martin Webster was a leading National Front politician of the 1970s.

Chapter 4

1. Caplan, G. 1964. *Principles of Preventive Psychiatry*. New York, Basic Books.

2. Yule, W. 1980. Handicap. *In* P. Feldman and J. Orford (eds). *Psychological Problems: the Social Context*. Chichester, Wiley, Chapter 8.

3. Orford, J. 1992. *Community Psychology: Theory and Practice*. Chichester, Wiley, Chapter 8.

4. Newton, J. 1988. *Preventing Mental Illness*. London, Routledge.

5. Chadwick, P.K. 1993. The stepladder to the impossible: A first-hand phenomenological account of a schizoaffective psychotic crisis. *Journal of Mental Health*, vol. 2, pp. 239-50.

6. Bebbington, P. and Kuipers, L. 1988. Social influences on schizophrenia. *In* P. Bebbinton and P. McGuffin *Schizophrenia: The major issues*. Oxford, Heinemann, Chapter 15.

7. Campo, V. 1977. Paranoia, Nixon and psychiatry. *Newscribes*, vol. 2, Pt 1-2, pp. 8-12.

8. Heller, K. 1988. Research Hypotheses for Intervention with Delusion-Prone Individuals. *In* T.F. Oltmanns and B.A. Maher. *Delusional Beliefs*. New York, Wiley, Chapter 15.

9. Leff, J. 1991. Schizophrenia: social influences on onset and relapse. *In* D.H. Bennett and H.L. Freeman (eds.) *Community Psychiatry*. Churchill Livingstone, Chapter 6.

10. Chadwick, P.K. 1992. *Borderline: A psychological study of paranoia and delusional thinking*. London, Routledge, pp. 113-115.

11. Sutherland, S. 1992. *Irrationality: The Enemy Within*. London, Constable, Chapter 10.

12. Chadwick, P.K. 1992. *Borderline (op. cit.)* p.81.

13. Federn, P. 1977. *Ego Psychology and the Psychoses*. London, Maresfield Reprints.

14. Chapman, L.J. and Chapman, J.P. 1969. Illusory correlation as an obstacle to the use of valid psychodiagnostic signs. *Journal of Abnormal Psychology*, vol. 74, pp. 271-80.

15. Marks, D. and Kamman, R. 1980. *The Psychology of the Psychic*. Buffalo, New York, Prometheus Books.

16. Johnson, M.K. 1988. Discriminating the origin of information. *In* T.F. Oltmanns and B.A. Maher, *Delusional Beliefs*. New York, Wiley, Chapter 3, pp. 49-53.

17. Hasher, L., Goldstein, D., and Toppiro, T. 1977. Frequency and the conference of referential validity. *Journal of Verbal Learning and Verbal Behaviour*, vol. 16, pp. 107-12.

18. Gittings, R. 1966. *Selected Poems and Letters of John Keats*. London, Heinemann, p.7.

19. Sutherland, S. 1992. *Irrationality (op. cit.)*, Chapter 10.

20. Chadwick, P.K. 1992. *Borderline (op. cit.)* p.119.

21. Huq, S.F., Garety, P. and Hemsley, D.R. 1988. Probabilistic judgements in deluded and non-deluded subjects. *Quarterly Journal of Experimental Psychology*, vol. 40A, pp. 801-12.

22. Tvesky, A. and Kahneman, D. 1983. Availability: a heuristic for judging frequency and probability. *Cognitive Psychology*, vol. 5, pp. 207-32.

23. Nisbett, R., and Ross, L. 1980. *Human Inference: Strategies and short-comings of social judgement*. Englewood Cliffs, New Jersey, Prentice-Hall.

24. Johnson, M.K. 1988. Discriminating the origin of information *(op. cit)*, pp. 40-46.

25. Sutherland, S. 1992. *Irrationality (op. cit.)*, pp. 25-8.

26. See, for example, Chapter 5 on Person Perception in A.L Weber, 1992. *Social Psychology*, New York, HarperCollins.

27. Kaney, S and Bentall,. R.P. 1989. Persecutory delusions and attributional style. *British Journal of Medical Psychology*, vol. 62, pp. 191-8.

28. Chadwick, P.K. 1992. *Borderline (op. cit.)*, pp.119-121.

29. Sass, L.A. 1994. *The Paradoxes of Delusion: Wittgenstein, Schreber and the Schizophrenic Mind*. Ithaca and London, Cornell University Press.

30. Chadwick, P.K. 1992. *Borderline (op. cit.)* p.88.

31. Federn, P. 1977. *Ego psychology and the psychoses (*op. cit.*).*

32. Weiner, B. 1992. *Human Motivation: Metaphors, Theories and Research.* California, Sage.

33. Johnson, W.G., Ross, J.M. and Mastria, M.A. 1977. Delusional behaviour. An attributional analysis of development and modification. *Journal of Abnormal Psychology*, vol. 86, pp.421-6.

34. Chadwick, P.K. 1992. *Borderline (op. cit.)*, pp.92-94.

Chapter 5

1. Burns, R.B. 1979. *The Self Concept in Theory: Measurement, Development and Behaviour.* London, Longman.

2. Rogers, C.R. 1967. *On Becoming a Person: A therapist's view of psychotherapy.* London, Constable.

3. Bentall, R.P., Kinderman, P., and Kaney. S. 1994. The Self, Attributional processes and abnormal beliefs: Towards a model of persecutory delusions. *Behaviour Research and Therapy*, vol. 32, no. 3, pp. 331-341.

   Haigh, G. 1949. Defensive behaviour in client-centred therapy. *Journal of Consulting Psychology.* vol. 13, pp. 181-89.

   Susan Hingley of the University of Newcastle also discusses the defensive function of persecutory delusions, in the context of the possibility that the boundary between the conscious and unconscious is weakened in paranoia sufferers. She thus sees a pathway to integrating cognitive and psychodynamic perspectives. An outline of her ideas is given in:

   Hingley, S. 1994. Psychological theories of delusional thinking: a synthesis. *Clinical Psychology Forum*, May, pp.41-42.

4. Pervin, L.A. 1993. *Personality: Theory and Research.* Chichester, Wiley, p.218.

5. Kihlstrom, J.F., and Cantor, N. 1984. Mental representation of the self. *In* L. Berkowitz (ed.) *Advances in Experimental Social Psychology*, vol. 17, pp. 1-47. London Academic Press.

6. Havener, P.H., and Izard, C.E. 1962. Unrealistic self-enhancement in paranoid schizophrenics. *Journal of Consulting Psychology*, vol. 26, pp.65-68.

7. Lyon, H.M., Kaney, S. and Bentall, R.P. 1994. The defensive function of persecutory delusions: evidence from attribution tasks. *British Journal of Psychiatry*, vol. 164, pp. 637-46.

8. Power, M.J. and Brewin, C.R. 1990. Self esteem regulation in an emotional priming task. *Cognition and Emotion*, vol. 4, Issue 1, March, pp.39-51.

9. Lyon, H.M. Kaney, S. and Bentall, R.P. 1994 (*op. cit.*).

10. Ditto.

11. Power, M. and Brewin, C. 1991. From Freud to cognitive science: a contemporary account of the unconscious. *British Journal of Clinical Psychology*, vol. 30, pp. 289-310.

12. Candido, C. and Romney, D.M. 1990. Attributional style in paranoid vs. depressed patients. *British Journal of Medical Psychology*, vol. 63, pp. 335-63.

13. Lyon, H.M., Kaney, S. and Bentall, R.P. 1994 (*op. cit.*), p.641.

14. Harper, D.J. 1992. Defining delusion and the serving of professional interests. The case of 'paranoia'. *British Journal of Medical Psychology*, vol. 65, pp. 357-69.

15. Valone, K., Norton J.P., Goldstein, M.J. and Doane, J.A. 1983. Parental expressed emotion and affective style in an adolescent sample at risk of schizophrenia spectrum disorders. *Journal of Abnormal Psychology*, vol. 92, pp. 279-85.

16. Freud, S. 1911. Psychoanalytic notes on an autobiographical account of a case of paranoia (dementia paranoides). *Standard Edition* vol. 12. London, Hogarth Press, pp.3-82.

17. Bentall, R.P., Kinderman, P. and Kaney, S. 1994 (*op. cit.*), p. 335.

18. Fenigstein, A. and Vanable, P.A. 1992. Paranoia and self consciousness. *Journal of Personality and Social Psychology*, vol. 62, pp. 129-34.

19. Lyon, H.M., Kaney, S. and Bentall, R.P. 1994 (*op. cit.*), pp. 642-43.

20. Thalbourne, M.A. 1994. Belief in the paranormal and its relationship to schizophrenia-relevant measures: A confirmatory study. *British Journal of Clinical Psychology*, vol. 33, Pt 1. February, pp.78-80.
    A range of factors influencing belief in the paranormal, including personality factors and issues of mental disturbance, are given in:
    Irwin, H.J. 1993. Belief in the paranormal: a review of the empirical literature. *The Journal of the American Society for Psychical Research*, vol. 87, no. 1, January, especially pp. 22-31.

21. Chadwick, P.K. *Borderliners: Human experience at the outer limits of sanity — and beyond.* (In preparation)

22. Marks, D. and Kamman, R. 1980. *The Psychology of the Psychic.* Buffalo, New York, Prometheus Books.

23. Palmer, J. 1971. Scoring in ESP tests as a function of belief in ESP. Part 1: The sheep-goat effect. *The Journal of the American Society for Psychical Research*. vol. 65, no 4, October, pp. 373-407.

24. Chadwick, P.K. 1992. *Borderline: A psychological study of paranoia and delusional thinking*. London, Routledge, p. 100.
Research which overviews the cognitive or thinking biases that encourage and maintain belief in the paranormal is given in:
French, C.C. 1992. Factors underlying belief in the paranormal: Do sheep and goats think differently? *The Psychologist*, vol. 5, pp. 295-99.

25. Chadwick, P.K. 1992 *Borderline (op. cit.)*, p.112.

26. Ditto, pp. 98-104.

27. Ditto, pp. 120-124.

28. Davison, G.C. and Neale, J.M. 1994. *Abnormal Psychology*. New York, Wiley, p.254.

29. Milton, F., Patwa, U.K. and Hafner, J. 1978. Confrontation vs. belief modification in persistently deluded patients. *British Journal of Medical Psychology*, vol. 51, pp. 127-30.

30. Chadwick, P.K. 1992. *Borderline (op. cit)* p. 143.

31. Rudden, M., Gilmore, M. and Frances, A. 1982. Delusions: When to confront the facts of life. *American Journal of Psychiatry*, vol. 134, no. 7 (July), pp. 924-32.

32. Chadwick, P.D.J. and Lowe, C.F. 1990. Measurement and Modification of Delusional Beliefs. *Journal of Consulting and Clinical Psychology*, vol. 58, no. 2, pp. 225-32.

33. Chadwick, P.K. *Borderline (op. cit.)* p. 142.

34. Watts, F.N., Powell, E.G. and Austin, S.V. 1973. The modification of abnormal beliefs. *British Journal of Medical Psychology*, vol. 46, pp. 359-63.

35. Freeman, N.H., Sinha, C.G. and Stedman, J.A. 1982. 'All the cars – which cars? From word meaning to discourse analysis'. *In* M. Beveridge (ed.) *Children Thinking Through Language*. London, Edward Arnold.

36. Watts, F.N., Powell, E.G. and Austin, S.V. 1973 *(op. cit.)*.

37. Chadwick, P.D.J. and Lowe, C.F. 1990 *(op. cit.)*.

38. Ditto *(op. cit.)*, p. 230.

39. Ditto *(op. cit.)*.

40. Fowler, D.G., Garety, P.A., Kuipers L. and Chamberlain, F. 1994.

The relationships between theory and therapy of delusions: A series of single case investigations. *British Journal of Medical Psychology* (in press).

41. Greyson, B. 1977. Telepathy in mental illness: Deluge or Delusion? *The Journal of Nervous and Mental Disease*, vol. 165, pp. 184-200.

42. Bentall, R.P., Kinderman, P. and Kaney, S. 1994 (*op. cit.*), p.338.

43. Chadwick, P.K. 1992. *Borderline (op. cit.*), pp. 145-46.

44. Thorne, B. 1990. Person-centred therapy. *In* W. Dryden (ed.) *Individual Therapy: A handbook*, Milton Keynes, Open University Press, Chapter 6, pp. 104-126.

45. Slade, P.D., and Bentall, R.P. 1988. *Sensory Deception: A scientific analysis of hallucinations.* London, Croom Helm.

46. Boyle, M. 1990. *Schizophrenia: A scientific delusion?* London, Routledge, pp. 198-200.
    See also: Strauss, J.S. 1969. Hallucinations and delusions as points on continua: rating-scale evidence. *Archives of General Psychiatry*, vol. 21, pp. 581-86.

47. Alpert, M. 1985. The signs and symptoms of schizophrenia. *Comprehensive Psychiatry*, vol. 26, pp. 103-112.

48. Recent research on hallucinations and its relevance to therapy is also overviewed in two papers by Richard Bentall and his colleagues. These are:
    Bentall, R.P. 1990. The Illusion of Reality: A review and integration of psychological research on hallucinations. *Psychological Bulletin,* vol. 107, no 1, pp. 82-95.
    Bentall, R.P., Haddock, G. and Slade, P.D. 1994. Cognitive-Behaviour therapy for persistent auditory hallucinations. *Behaviour Therapy*, vol. 25, pp. 51-66.

49. Chadwick, P.K. 1992. *Borderline (op. cit.)*, pp. 79-81.

50. Johnson, D.A.W. 1988. Drug treatment of schizophrenia. *In* P. Bebbington and P. McGuffin. *Schizophrenia: The Major Issues.* Oxford, Heinemann, Chapter 2, pp. 158-171.

51. Chadwick, P.K. 1992. *Borderline (op. cit.)*, p.78. (See also: Feder, R. 1982. Auditory hallucinations treated by radio headphones. *American Journal of Psychiatry.* vol. 139, no 9, September, pp. 1188-90.) More techniques for reducing hallucinations can be found in Peter Slade's Chapter 9 *in* R.P. Bentall (ed.) 1990. *Reconstructing Schizophrenia.* London, Routledge, pp. 234-253.

52. Sekuler, R. and Blake, R., 1985. *Perception*. New York, Alfred A. Knopf, Chapter 12, pp. 421-48.

53. Skinner, B.F. 1957. *Verbal Behaviour*. New York, Appleton-Century-Crofts.

54. Chadwick, P.K. 1992. *Borderline (op. cit.)*, pp. 91-92.

55. Gregory, R.L. 1987. Perception. *In* R.L. Gregory (ed.) *The Oxford Companion to the Mind*. Oxford, Oxford University Press, pp. 598-601.

56. Gregory, R.L. 1970. *The Intelligent Eye*. New York, McGraw Hill.

57. Chadwick, P.K. 1988. *A psychological study of paranoia and delusional thinking*. Doctorate dissertation, Royal Holloway and Bedford New College, University of London, pp. 302-303.

58. La Russo, L. 1978. Sensitivity of paranoid patients to non-verbal cues. *Journal of Abnormal Psychology*, vol. 87, no. 5, October, pp. 463-71.

59. At a 1994 neuroscience conference on consciousness in Mexico, Dr Jacobo Grinberg of the National University of Mexico reported tests on the effects of strong empathic links between couples. When one person of the pair was isolated in a Faraday cage (to block out all electromagnetic radiation), subjected to stimuli such as mild electric shocks and the responses of their brains to the stimuli monitored, it was found that the brain response of *the other member of the pair* was remarkably similar – even though they were separated from their partner, had *not* been subjected to the stimuli and were not even aware of them. This result, which clearly needs to be reproduced, nonetheless raises serious questions about conventional scientific models of mind.

60. May, R.M. 1993. *Cosmic Consciousness Revisited: The Modern Origins and Development of a Western Spiritual Psychology*. Dorset, Element Books.

Chapter 6

1. This is the inescapable conclusion from two critical papers: one by Gordon Claridge, 'Can a disease model of schizophrenia survive?' and one by Nicholas Tarrier, 'The family management of schizophrenia'. These are chapters 6 and 10 in Richard Bentall's edited volume *Reconstructing Schizophrenia* (Routledge, 1990).

2. A general discussion of toxic drug effects is given in Peter Breggin's

Toxic Psychiatry (Fontana, 1993).

3. See D.A.W. Johnson's chapter 'Drug treatment of schizophrenia' (chapter 12, especially pp. 167-68) in Paul Bebbington and Peter McGuffin's *Schizophrenia: The Major Issues* (Heinemann, 1988). See also the discussion of the side-effects of the relatively new drug, Clozapine, by Stephen Stahl and Kathleen Wets (chapter 11, pp. 142-44) in the same volume.

4. See: Bentall, R.P., Jackson, H.F. and Pilgrim, D. 1988, Abandoning the concept of 'schizophrenia'. *British Journal of Clinical Psychology*, vol. 27, pp. 303-324, and also: Warner, R. 1985 *Recovery from Schizophrenia: Psychiatry and Political Economy*. London, Routledge.

5. Vaughn C. and Leff, J.P. 1976. Influence of family and social factors on the course of psychiatric illness. *British Journal of Psychiatry*, vol. 129, pp. 125-137.

6. Leff, J.P. and Vaughn C. 1981. The role of maintenance therapy and relatives' expressed emotion in the relapse of schizophrenia: a two-year follow-up. *British Journal of Psychiatry*, vol. 139, pp. 102-104.

7. Leff, J.P. 1991. Schizophrenia: social influences on onset and relapse. *In* D.H. Bennett and H.L. Freeman (eds.), *Community Psychiatry*. Churchill Livingstone, Chapter 6, pp. 189-214.
    See also Brooker, C. 1990. *Community Psychiatric Nursing*, London. Chapman and Hall.

8. Warner, R. 1985. *Recovery from Schizophrenia: Psychiatry and Political Economy*. London, Routledge.

9. Davison, G.C. and Neale, J.M. 1994. *Abnormal Psychology*. New York, John Wiley, chapter 14, pp. 418-19.

10. Kuipers, L., Birchwood, M. and McCreadie, R.D. 1992. Psychosocial family intervention in schizophrenia: A review of empirical studies. *British Journal of Psychiatry*, vol. 160, pp. 272-275

11. Hogarty, G.E., Anderson, C.M., Reiss, D.J. et al. 1991. Family psychoeducation, social skills training and maintenance chemotherapy in the aftercare treatment of schizophrenia. *Archives of General Psychiatry*, vol. 48, pp. 340-347.

12. Johnstone, L. 1993. Family management in 'schizophrenia': its assumptions and contradictions. *Journal of Mental Health*, vol. 2, pp. 255-269.

13. Falloon, I., McGill, C. and Boyd, J. 1984. *Family Care of Schizophrenia*. New York, Guilford Press.

See also Seeman, M.V., Littman, S.K. et al. 1982. *Living and Working with Schizophrenia*. Milton Keynes, Open University Press.

14. Chadwick, P.K. 1993. The stepladder to the impossible: a first-hand phenomenological account of a schizoaffective psychotic crisis. *Journal of Mental Health*, vol. 2, pp. 239-250.

15. Brown, G.W., Birley, J.L.T. and Wing, J.K. 1972. Influence of family life on the course of schizophrenic disorders: a replication. *British Journal of Psychiatry,* vol. 121, pp. 241-258.

16. Johnstone, L. 1993, *op. cit.*

17. See both Nicholas Tarrier 1990 (*op. cit.*) and Peter Breggin 1993 (*op. cit.*)

18. The neglect of the real *psychology* underlying patients' behaviour and its conceptualization in terms of 'symptoms' of an organic disorder to be 'managed' is clear in J. Smith and M. Birchwood's 1985 booklet *Understanding Schizophrenia* (West Birmingham Health Authority).

19. Doane, J.A., West, K.L., Goldstein, M.J. et al., 1981. Parental communicative deviance and affective style. *Archives of General Psychiatry*, vol. 38, pp. 679-715 *and* Valone, K., Goldstein, M.J. and Norton, J.P. 1984. Parental expressed emotion and psychophysiological reactivity in an adolescent sample at risk for schizophrenia spectrum disorders. *Journal of Abnormal Psychology* vol. 93, pp. 448-457.

20. Brown, G.W., Birley J.L.T. and Wing, J.K. 1972, *op. cit.*

21. That the EE level of the home is not centrally a reaction to the disturbed behaviour of the patient, is shown by the fact that disturbance of behaviour on admission is *negatively* related to relapse. Numerous studies, however, have found that if EE is statistically controlled the association between disturbed behaviour and relapse falls to zero. These studies therefore critically implicate EE as a factor influencing the course of schizophrenia. (See, for example, Julian Leff's 1991 chapter 'Schizophrenia: social influences on onset and relapse' in Bennett and Freeman's *Community Psychiatry (op. cit.)*. The Doane and Valone papers (see note 19) also have the same implication – high EE is *not* a reaction to patient behaviour; it has causal properties.

22. Gottesman, I., and Shield, J. 1972. *Schizophrenia and genetics: a twin study vantage point*. New York, Academic Press *and* Gottesman, I.,

McGuffin, P. and Farmer, A.E. 1987. Clinical genetics as a clue to the 'real' genetics of schizophrenia. *Schizophrenia Bulletin*, vol. 13, pp. 23-47.

23. High EE parents or partners are variously described as over-involved, over-protective, hostile, critical, controlling and overly self-sacrificial. In my book *Borderline* I outlined the existentially destructive character of some such people by prising open the basic psychological *mottos* involved. Below is a slightly modified version of this scheme of mottos.

   On the patronizing over-involved 'schizophrenogenic' parent:

   You see, I'm in a position to criticize you repeatedly, because I am your superior, I am right, you are wrong. You are the 'looked-after' one, it is I who is the 'looker after'. I am dominant, you submissive, I talk, you listen, I am adult-like, you child-like, I know what's best, but you don't. I can deal with life, I can face life, you can't. This is because I am masterful, competent, but you are not. You see, in secret, what it boils down to is that you are my punch bag and my lovely looked-after lump of custard pie. As long as you are around I will be right, adult, in control, competent, able to get by in life, good and strong! It will always be I who is the willer, while you are the willed. This way I exist, am substantial. You do not. Compared to ME, you're empty, nothing, a hole in space. This is the way I like it. You see, the fact of the matter is: I AM . . . you are not.

                          P.K. Chadwick *Borderline* (Routledge, 1992), p. 63.

24. Berkowitz, R. 1984. Therapeutic intervention with schizophrenic patients and their families: a description of a clinical research project. *Journal of Family Therapy*, vol. 6., pp. 211-233.
25. Berkowitz, R. 1984. (*op. cit.*)
26. Chadwick, P.K. 1992. *Borderline (op. cit.),* p. 63.
27. Vaughn C. and Leff, J.P. 1976. (*op. cit.*).
28. Chadwick, P.K. 1993 (*op. cit.*), p. 248.
29. Davison, G.C. and Neale, J.M. 1986. *Abnormal Psychology*. New York, John Wiley.
30. Eysenck, H. J. 1956. The Inheritance of Extroversion-Introversion. *Acta Psychologica*, vol. 12, pp. 95-110.
31. Johnson, M.K. 1988. Discriminating the origin of information. *In* T.F. Oltmanns and B.A. Maher, *Delusional Beliefs*. New York, John Wiley, Chapter 3, p. 49.

32. Eysenck, H.J. 1981. *A Model for Personality*. New York, Springer-Verlag, Chapter 1, especially pp. 17-19.

33. Chadwick, P.K. 1992. *Borderline (op. cit.)*, p. 94.

34. La Russo, L. 1978. Sensitivity of paranoid patients to non-verbal cues. *Journal of Abnormal Psychology*, vol. 87, no. 5, October, pp. 463-71.

35. Bleuler, M. 1978. *The Schizophrenic Disorders. Long-term Patient and Family Studies*. New Haven, Yale University Press.

36. Chadwick, P.K. 1992. *Borderline, (op. cit.)*, pp. 120-123.

37. *ditto*, pp. 120-123.

38. Glucksberg, S. 1962. The influence of strength of drive on functional fixedness and perceptual recognition. *Journal of Experimental Psychology*, vol. 63, pp. 36-41.

39. Easterbrook, J.A. 1959. The effect of emotion on cue utilization and the organization of behaviour. *Psychological Review*, vol. 66, pp. 183-201.

40. Chadwick, P.K. 1992. *Borderline (op. cit.)* pp. 115-116.

41. *ditto*, p. 116.

42. *ditto*, p. 127.

43. *ditto* pp. 125-126.

44. La Russo, L. 1978 *(op. cit.)*

45. Rushton. J. P., Fulker, D.W., Neale, M.C., Blizard, R.A. and Eysenck, H.J. 1984, Altruism and Genetics. *Acta. Genet. Med. Gemellol*, vol. 33, pp. 265-271.

46. Benjafield, J. and Green, T.R.G. 1978. Golden Section relations in interpersonal judgements. *British Journal of Psychology*, vol. 69, no. 1, pp. 23-35.
    (The Greek 'Golden Section' is the aesthetically ideal ratio for the short to long sides of a rectangle often used to guide architectural design. The critical ratio is 0.61.)

47. Coupland, N. and Coupland, J. 1990. Language and later life. *In* H. Giles and W.P. Robinson (eds.) *Handbook of Language and Social Psychology*. Chichester, John Wiley. See also Gillian Cohen's comments in *The Psychologist*, October 1992, vol. 5, no. 10, p. 449.

48. Birchwood, M. 1992. Early intervention in schizophrenia: Theoretical background and clinical strategies. *British Journal of Clinical Psychology*, vol. 31, pp. 257-278.
    More accessible for the reader is the book by M. Birchwood and N.

Tarrier (1992), *Innovations in the Psychological Management of Schizophrenia*. Chichester; Wiley.

49. Harper, D.J. 1994. The professional construction of 'paranoia' and the discursive use of diagnostic criteria. *British Journal of Medical Psychology*, vol. 67. pp. 131-143 and pp 151-153.

50. Allyon, T. and Haughton, E. 1964. Modification of symptomatic behaviour of mental patients. *Behaviour Research and Therapy*, vol. 2. pp. 87-89.

51. Orford, J. (ed.) 1987. *Coping with Disorder in the Family*. London, Sydney, Croom Helm.

52. Birchwood, M and Smith, J. 1987. Schizophrenia and the family. *In* J. Orford (ed.) *Coping with Disorder in the Family (op. cit.)* Chapter 2, pp. 7-38.

Chapter 7

1. Claridge, G.S. 1993. What is schizophrenia? Common theories and divergent views. *Journal of Mental Health*, vol. 2, no. 3, September, pp. 251-53.

2. Berrios, G. 1991. Delusions as 'wrong beliefs': a conceptual history. *British Journal of Psychiatry*, vol. 159, pp. 6-13.

3. Gordon-Browne, I. and Somers, B. 1988. Transpersonal Psychotherapy. *In* J. Rowan and W. Dryden (eds.) *Innovative Therapy in Britain*. Milton Keynes, Open University Press, Chapter 11, pp. 225-250.

4. Bechtel, W. and Abrahamsen, A, 1991. *Connectionism and the Mind; An Introduction to Parallel Processing in Networks*. Oxford, Basil Blackwell, Chapter 4.

5. Barham, P. and Hayward, R. 1990. Schizophrenia as a Life Process. *In* R.P. Bentall (ed.) *Reconstructing Schizophrenia*. London, Routledge, Chapter 3.

6. Claridge, G.S. 1990. Can a disease model of schizophrenia survive? *In* R.P. Bentall (ed.) *Reconstructing Schizophrenia*. London, Routledge, Chapter 6.

7. Chadwick, P.K. 1992. *Borderline: A psychological study of paranoia and delusional thinking*. London, Routledge.

8. Chadwick, P.K. *Borderliners: Human experience at the outer limits of sanity — and beyond*. (In preparation)

9. Birchwood, M. and Smith, J. 1987. Schizophrenia and the Family. *In* J. Orford (ed.) *Coping with Disorder in the Family*. Chapter 2, pp. 7-38. London, Sydney, Croom Helm.

10. Bentall, R.P. 1993. Personality traits may be alive, they may even be well, but are they really useful? *The Psychologist*, vol. 6, no. 7, July p. 307.

11. Thomson, M. 1989. *On Art and Therapy: An exploration*. London, Virago.

12. Alexandrian, S. 1970. *Surrealist Art*. London, Thames and Hudson.

13. Horgan, J. 1992. Quantum Philosophy. *Scientific American*, vol. 267, no. 1, July, pp. 72-80.

14. Bohr, N. 1958. *Atomic Theory and Human Knowledge*. New York, Wiley.

15. Bentall, R.P. 1990. Schizophrenia – a suitable case for treatment? *In* R.P. Bentall (ed.) *Reconstructing Schizophrenia*. London, Routledge, pp. 283-296.

16. Johnstone, L. 1993. Family management in 'schizophrenia': its assumptions and contradictions. *Journal of Mental Health*, vol. 2, no. 3, September, pp. 253-69.

17. Chapman, L.J. and Chapman, J.P. 1969. Illusory correlation as an obstacle to the use of valid psychodiagnostic signs. *Journal of Abnormal Psychology*, vol. 74, pp. 271-280.

18. Lusted, L.B. 1968. *Introduction to Medical Decision-making*. Illinois, Charles C. Thomas.
    See also:
    Chadwick, P.K. 1977. Scientists can have illusions too. *New Scientist*, vol. 73, 31 March, pp. 768-71.
    Kundel, H.L. and Nodine, C.F. 1983. A visual concept shapes image perception. *Radiology*, vol. 146, pp. 363-68.

INDEX